ACROSS THE
FOOTSTEPS
OF AFRICA

ACROSS THE FOOTSTEPS OF AFRICA

The Experiences of an Ecuadorian Doctor in Malawi and Mozambique

Benjamin Puertas Donoso

Africa World Press, Inc.

P.O. Box 1892
Trenton, NJ 08607

P.O. Box 48
Asmara, ERITREA

Africa World Press, Inc.

P.O. Box 1892
Trenton, NJ 08607

P.O. Box 48
Asmara, ERITREA

Copyright © 1999 Benjamin Puertas Donoso

First Africa World Press edition, 1999
From the Spanish edition, *Tras las huellas de Africa*
Translated by Dorothy J. Swartz

Book Design: Krystal Jackson
Cover Design: Jonathan Gullery

Library of Congress Cataloging-in-Publication Data

Puertas D., Benjamin.
     [Tras las huellas de Africa. English]
     Across the footsteps of Africa : the experiences of an Ecuadorian doctor in Malawi and Mozambique / by Benjamin Puertas Donoso.
     p.   cm.
     ISBN 0-86543-639-8 (hardcover). --ISBN 0-86543-640-1 (pbk.)
     1. Physicians--Mozambique.   2. Physicians--Malawi.   3. Missions, Medical--Malawi.   4. Missions,   Medical--Mozambique.
RA395.M85P8413 1998
610'.92--dc21
[B]   98-34380
                                                                      CIP

Dedication

To my parents, Fanny and Benjamín,
for their constant support and encouragement.

The publication of this book is possible thanks to the collaborative efforts of several individuals on three continents who unselfishly gave their support in order to turn it into a reality. To enumerate them would be lengthy, but I would like to mention a few: Mónica León, John and Dorothy Swartz, Jeff Swartz, Conny C. Arvis, Bashir Sacranie, Mirta Steffen, Mitchel Strumpf, each of whom played an invaluable role. In addition, I extend my most sincere gratitude and appreciation to the thousands of Mozambican refugees, whose dramatic existence was a constant source of inspiration. May all their sacrifices not be in vain.

—Benjamín Puertas Donoso

CONTENTS

PART ONE

PART TWO

PART THREE

FOREWORD

*The important thing is to construct your
life in order to make the life of others more
beautiful and happy without their applause.*

—Anonymous

The extraordinary experiences of the author during his
two years on the African continent, as a community doctor in the Mozambican refugee camps in Malawi and his
later experience in Mozambique have taken shape in a
perfect and gratifying manner in this work.

For a Latin American, the African continent is a distant and unknown place. However, the author's descriptions, that is, his use of rich, fluent, and authentic language, continue to transport us to that region of the
planet to explore the richness of its history and its people through details that denote deep investigation into
the social, cultural, and political aspects of young
nations that, for the most part, have passed through a
tortuous process of republican consolidation. What
remains from exploitation, discrimination, and racism
still prevail, marking a parallel to our own reality, in
spite of the great distance.

There is no doubt that the author's own mystique is
manifested in his continuing search for solutions to the
critical conditions of the refugees who are affected by the
most severe tropical illnesses that are exacerbated by a
precarious nutritional state and limited available
resources. Leaving his own country, with all the comforts of civilization and the advantages that these can
offer, in exchange for the harshness of countries at war,
the investigative spirit and the great personal courage of

Benjamin Puertas Donoso overcome all. An analogy of his motives evokes Mother Theresa's statement: "The feeling of duty is something very personal. It comes from knowing the need to undertake an action and not just the need to urge others to do something." This concept is well represented in *Across the Footsteps of Africa*.

It has been quite some time since I last read a book so stimulating and so full of magic and color. Its reader becomes enthralled, as much for those involved in the medical field, especially young students and new graduates, as for the common individual whose work takes place in other disciplines.

There is no doubt that it is not their titles but their actions that make men noble. The work of Benjamín Puertas stands as testimony, an example for future generations to follow.

—GONZALO MANTILLA, M.D., F.A.A.P.
Dean of the School of Health Sciences
Universidad San Francisco de Quito, Ecuador

INTRODUCTION

For many regions of the planet, the end of the cold war and the prevailing new economic order have not signified the beginning of an era of peace and production. Rather, ancient ethnic conflicts have been reactivated, and there exists a marked nationalist tendency that has brought about the disintegration of countries (e.g. former Yugoslavia), while tribal aggression has intensified, resulting in the macabre extreme such as the massacres between the Hutu and the Tutsi in Rwanda and Burundi.

As a consequence of these fratricidal wars, millions of people in the world have seen themselves obliged to abandon their homes, their countries, in order to search for protection in areas that offer greater security, thus turning themselves and their families into refugees. The civil war in Mozambique forced hundreds of thousands of individuals to escape the terror and violence of those long years; only in Malawi could a million Mozambicans set up residence in refugee camps along the length of the long common frontier. Not all refugees had the same luck, since other countries closed their frontiers, or the population gave a cold shoulder to the recent arrivals.

Several times during the months I worked in refugee camps, I tried to imagine myself as one of those unfortunate people: as someone without work, without home, and, as in many cases, without family to whom I could return. I always wound up abandoning the notion, for it was too hard and too cruel for me to bear. Complete dependence on external support turned many of those individuals into indolent beings, without initiative of their own, which was to become an enormous barrier that made eventual repatriation and the consequent return to "normality" enormously difficult. In the field of health, that passivity would negatively influence the execution of health programs in which community empowerment was a principal ingredient.

In an era of scientific development and technological advancement, it is incomprehensible that the exoduses of massive populations fleeing the horror of war can occur. It is difficult to explain the deaths of thousands of infants from easily prevented illnesses. It is painful to watch with impassivity the face of a marasmic child who soon will die for lack of food.

This book tries to humanize the tragedy of the refugees, bringing them closer to our reading table and placing them within the context of daily African occurrences. Several of the reports are lessons in life from individuals who have been cruelly displaced from everything that we consider essential; however, in all their misery they are capable of looking at the world with an optimism that you and I can only envy.

Benjamín Puertas Donoso

ACRONYMS

AFORD	Alliance for Democracy
ARC	American Refugee Committee
CO	Clinical Officer
DHO	District Health Officer
FRELIMO	Mozambican Liberation Front
GTZ	Deutsche Gesellschaft für Technische Zusammenarbeit
HI	Health Inspector
HSA	Health Surveillance Assistant
JRS	Jesuit Refugee Service
MA	Medical Assistant
MCP	Malawi Congress Party
MDP	Malawi Democratic Party
MDU	Malawi Democratic Union
MOH	Ministry of Health
MSF	Médecins Sans Frontières of France (called "Doctors Without Borders" in the United States)
MYP	Malawi Young Pioneers
NAC	Nyasaland African Congress
NGO	Nongovernmental Organization
ONUMOZ	United Nations Operations in Mozambique
RENAMO	National Mozambican Resistance
RHO	Regional Health Officer
UDF	United Democratic Front
UNHCR	United Nations High Commission for Refugees
UNICEF	United Nations International Children's Emergency Fund
UNFPA	United Nations Fund for Population Activities

UNPFM	United Nations Peace Force in Malawi
USAID	United States Agency for International Development

Other organizations without acronyms, referred to in the text:

International Eye Foundation
International Rescue Committee
Save the Children UK
World Vision

MAP OF AFRICA

Map of Africa, locating Malawi and Mozambique

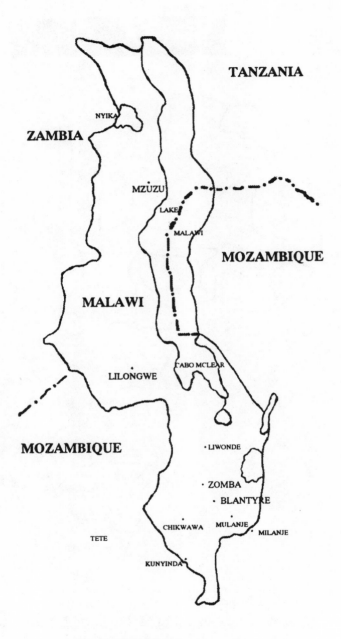

Map of Malawi

PART
ONE

1

NEW VENTURES

January 1993

The winter rain had turned the only land route that joined the Chang'ambika refugee camp to Mwanza, thirty miles (fifty kilometers) away, into an impassable quagmire. From there on, a first class asphalt highway united Mwanza with Blantyre, Malawi's principal city, yet another sixty-five miles (108 kilometers) beyond. The irregularities of the terrain worsened the situation, because a series of precipitous rises and falls in the Thambani Forest Reserve area made access more difficult, even dangerous in some stretches. The camp, with its 25,000 Mozambican refugees, was experiencing one of the worst epidemics of cholera and dysentery of recent times, averaging thirty to forty new cases a day. In spite of the continuous rehydration therapy and specific treatment administered in the Cholera and Dysentery Units, there had not been a single day in which a death had not been recorded.

The situation turned critical when the reserve of Ringer's Lactate (used in intravenous rehydration) ran out and the number of packets of oral rehydration solution was visibly running low. The death rate from dehydration would rise to alarming levels unless we received a new supply of these medicines—for which we had been desperately waiting for several weeks. On more than one occasion, the American Refugee Committee truck was unable to reach our camp because of the deteriorating state of the highway, and there was no indication that the weather would improve. The lack of means of communication was an additional factor that did not help to alleviate the situation.

Within the next few days we exhausted our reserve of Haemacell (a plasma expander) and saline solution, and we knew that in one or two days the oral salts would also run out. Meanwhile, the longed-for truck did not arrive. Our health team met and agreed that, as an emergency measure, we should have a quantity of salt, sugar, and bicarbonate ready to prepare a "home-made oral solution" in order to meet the crisis. We knew it was also only a temporary measure since the sugar and salt for this preparation would not last much longer....

In the next twenty-four hours we came to the conclusion that if we did not take other steps, the consequences would be disastrous in terms of an increase in mortality. Stanley Banda, the public health advisor, and myself, with our trusted driver Noel Mkandawire, set out in a four-wheel drive Toyota Land Cruiser on a one-day trip that was not certain to reach our destination, the Lisungwe camp in the district of Mwanza. There we were, hoping to obtain from Médecins Sans Frontières, the prestigious French organization known as MSF (in English, "Doctors Without Borders"), quantities of intravenous solutions—in the form of a loan—to get us past the emergency. In spite of the poor state of the road, there were no major mishaps in the initial stretch; but after arriving at the Thambani Forest Reserve we were stuck in mud on more than one occasion, especially as we began our ascent of Mount Thambani. With the aid of the local people who helped to push the truck out of a mudhole several times, we finally reached our destination, taking three times longer than when the road is in its best condition. After Mwanza, we had no difficulty in getting to Camp Lisungwe.

Guillermo Bertoletti, an Argentinean doctor and MSF's health coordinator for the refugee camps in the Mwanza district, did not hesitate to give us what he could, which in this case was twenty boxes, twelve lactates in each, and some five hundred packets of oral salts. I admit that being the only Latin Americans working in the area probably contributed to our relationship, and I hoped that this show of cooperation would be repeated in the future.

The return to Chang'ambika was even more difficult, and at times we doubted we would make it. With our valuable cargo in baskets, the descent from Mount Thambani gave us chills when, on one occasion, the vehicle lost its traction and slid dangerously toward the cliff, barely missing the edge of the precipice. Relying on the help of a towline, we were able to pull the vehicle out of several bogs when a tree was nearby so that we could secure the electric towline cable, extending it to the front part of the vehicle. At other times, it was necessary to resort to the hands-on strength of the locals in the vicinity. Our arrival in the camp was very emotional, especially for those few who were aware of our precious cargo. The supply was distributed immediately, and only those cholera patients who were at the point of severe dehydration received the maximum of three to four units of intravenous solutions. The rest received oral rehydration. Happily, at the time when the new supplies again began to run dangerously short, one truck was able to get through the enclosure that Mother Nature had placed around us, and it arrived with its valuable load, signaling the end of the first of the several crisis that we were to face.

In spite of our efforts during that month, we registered thirty as dying from cholera and dysentery. More than thirty-five deaths went unreported, and it is significant that more than 75 percent of these occurred in children under the age of five. However, considering the high number of cases that were reported in this one month (approximately five hundred), the fatality rate from cholera and dysentery was 6 percent, and in the following month, with an adequate supply of medication, the rate dropped to 2 percent. The Angel of Death slowly pulled away, although in truth it never completely left us.

AN OPPORTUNITY IS BORN

I had always had the feeling that my destiny would be forged, in part, in some remote and unknown land. I was working for Management Sciences for Health (MSH)[2] when I decided to submit a study about the evaluation of the immunization program that I had made in the province of Chimborazo (Ecuador) for consideration at the next National Council of International Health in Washington, D.C. (NCIH). Less than two months later I learned that it had been accepted. By then I was already working for the Ministry of Public Health (Promotion and Protection Direction) in Quito, fulfilling my year of *Medicina Rural*.[3] In June 1992, I traveled to the United States to present my work at the international meeting, to meet an old love from the past, and to apply for employment with several organizations that were participating in the conference.

There were several interviews with different organizations, the majority North American. One of those showed much interest in hiring me after the initial interview: American Refugee Committee (ARC), and I had more than one meeting with their representatives. ARC is a nongovernmental health emergency and relief organization based in Minneapolis that works with refugees and displaced populations in the U.S., Asia, Africa, and Europe (Bosnia). The place they first mentioned to me

6

was Cambodia, but I also knew of programs on other continents, including Africa. After returning to Ecuador, a series of telephone conversations and correspondence began in which ARC asked for more information, and, during these exchanges, they mentioned that one country in particular needed a doctor with public health experience immediately. It was then that I first learned the name of the country with which I soon would be tied for the next two years: Malawi.

By October 1992, I had a firm offer to work as the health coordinator for the district of Chikwawa in Malawi, and a little later a one-year contract arrived by Federal Express. My immediate presence was required. In less than two weeks, with a great deal of difficulty, I managed to make all the necessary arrangements for such a long journey. I began to experience the difficulties that Ecuadorian citizens have to face when traveling to Africa: Malawi has no embassy in Ecuador, and I needed a visa to enter the country. I had to send my passport to the U.S. via express mail in order to obtain the visa, and time was running out. I reserved my prepaid air ticket at the KLM office in Quito, and it indicated an exotic itinerary that included such places as Curazao, Amsterdam, Dar es Salaam and, finally, Lilongwe. To reach the capital of this little country of Malawi, it would take nearly two days, traveling through a seven-hour time-zone change, through those respective ports-of-call. While the direct distance between Quito and Lilongwe is 7,685 miles (12,396 kilometers), the total length of the trip was 10,800 miles (17,447 kilometers).

Holland was a true representation of the harsh winters of the north, and thanks only to the loan of a warm jacket from Sabine—a Dutch girl whom I knew only through descriptions from mutual friends—was it possible for me to withstand the cold during the one day I was in the capital. The stop at Dar es Salaam, the capital of Tanzania, gave me a good idea of what was coming. As opposed to Amsterdam, the temperature was approximately 100°F (38°C), the air terminal lacked ventilation, and there was no water in the bathrooms. Fortunately, it was only one-hour stopover. It surprised me to see that the majority of the passengers on the plane were white, most of them headed for Lilongwe. Afterwards I calculated the number of hours I was flying in a plane, twenty-four all told, without counting the stops at airports or the time spent in them.

Malawi, also known as "Africa for Beginners," surprised me with its modern air terminal. Upon arrival I almost committed my first error by attempting to take a photograph of this international airport, called Kamuzu, which is considered a restricted zone. Another curiosity is that women of every age, before disembarking, would take what looked like a large scarf and wear it as a skirt, or they would change their slacks for a dress that extended below their knees. A little later I would learn that Malawi's dress code did not permit any woman—local or foreign—to be seen in pants. Men, however, were obliged to wear their hair short, a detail I had already anticipated.

MALAWI: "THE WARM HEART OF AFRICA"

Malawi, a small nation of scarcely 45,735 square miles (118,484 square kilometers), Lake Malawi comprising one-third of it, is located in the southeastern part of the African continent. With approximately ten million inhabitants, an average of 268 per square mile, it is one of the countries with the highest population density on the continent. In Ecuador, there are 107 inhabitants per square mile; in the United States, there are 74 per square mile. A land-locked country, Malawi is bordered on the north by Tanzania, on the west by Zambia, and on the south, east and southeast by Mozambique. These are no natural boundaries, since the country was formed during the past century as a result of the alliance between several native tribes and the British colonists. The oldest known inhabitants are a race of pygmies, the Kafula, followed later by the Bantu, who originally came from Cameroon. Around the thirteenth century, the Maravi ancestors migrated to the area from the Congo River basins and by the sixteenth century established an empire that embraced Zambia, the central and southern parts of Malawi, and the northern part of Mozambique. The Maravi are subdivided into three principal groups: the Sena, the Mang'anja, and the Chewa. Other groups (the Tumbuka and the Tonga) also established themselves in the central zone. In the nineteenth century, the Ngoni, who had fled the power of the bellicose Zulus, migrated to what is known today as Ntcheu.

In 1859, David Livingstone, the Scottish missionary, sailed up the Shire River until he found Lake Malawi. His battle against slavery caused him to make several trips into this part of Africa, where he subsequently established some missions, including the one in Blantyre named after Livingstone's birthplace. This mission, founded in 1876, was from the outset a medical one. The site was chosen for its great distance from the slave route that ran to Mulanje and Quelimane. In order to defend colonial interests, the British Protectorate of Nyasaland was created on May 14, 1891. Later, in 1944, the Nyasaland African Congress (NAC) was formed to give voice to an increasing opposition to the Federation of Rhodesia and Nyasaland, which had been imposed on the people by the British government.

The opposition gathered strength with the participation of a medical doctor who would be forever tied to the history of the country: Dr. Hastings Kamuzu Banda. Born in 1906 in Mtunthama, a village near Kasungu, he left at the age of thirteen for South Africa, where he began his studies. Later he traveled to the United States, where he graduated from medical school in 1937. He then continued his medical studies at the University of Edinburgh. After his return to Malawi in 1958, he organized the opposition until the British authorities jailed him. In 1960, he gained his liberty and was soon elected president of NAC, a position he held until July 6, 1964, when Nyasaland finally became the independent state of Malawi. In 1966, Dr. Banda became the first president of the Republic of Malawi. From then on the country was held under the totalitarian regime of the only party officially accepted in the country, the Malawi Congress Party, better known as the MCP. For decades no one questioned the supremacy of the party led by Dr. Banda, who, little by little, became intoxicated with power, thus losing contact with the people. Because of his advanced age (of more than ninety years), the reins of government were passed to John Tembo, a man whose name would henceforth be linked with the main events of the nation.

It did not take much time to comprehend the reasons for the fear that Tembo generated with most of the public. M. Munthali, a Malawian journalist, attributes to both Banda and Tembo dreadful human rights abuses ranging from "detention without trial, disappearances, torture in custody, judicial interference, punitive confiscation of property, sexual and work-related exploitation of women, dismissal from work, and complete controls of freedom of expression and religion." The human rights abuses, which touched every family, village, district, and region of the country, were also tied to the Malawi Young Pioneers, an armed group that answered only to the MCP and, more specifically, to Tembo. This group used intimidation and torture tactics against all those who valiantly expressed any objection to Banda's regime. Tembo, as Malawi's Prime Minister, became one of the most powerful and most feared individuals in the country, not only among the Africans but also among the expatriates, who ran the risk of expulsion from the country within twenty-four hours if they "interfered in the matters of internal security."

FIRST EXPERIENCES

My early premonitions that the trip to unknown Malawi was going to have a good beginning came to fruition. On my first day there, December 10, 1992, it rained, a novelty in an area that was suffering from one of its worst dry spells in recent times.

John Keys, director of the American Refugee Committee (ARC) in Malawi, was waiting for us at the airport. The "us" in this phrase included Betty Lee, a hearty North American nurse with wide experience in countries like Indonesia, Pakistan, and the United States, who would be one of the nurses in the Chikwawa district. I was a little surprised to see that we were dealing with a lady more than seventy years old. It's interesting to note that on the very day of my arrival I began to experience for myself the courtesies Africans extend toward white people. The drivers, baggage porters, and sales people all used terms like "master" or *"bwana"* and were eager to ease any stress on the part of the expatriate.

The American Refugee Committee's guesthouse is in an idyllic location on the shore of the Shire River in the town of Liwonde, and, until only recently, its main office was located there as well. I spent the long night in a deep sleep, lulled by the murmur of the river that ran only a few steps from my assigned cabin, recuperating from the long trip and jet lag. The only thing I heard that night was the splashing noise of the hippopotamus. I went on my first safari that same Saturday, visiting the Liwonde National Park, where I admired, at close range and for the first time, the fascinating wildlife that had given this con-tinent some of its well-deserved fame: mandrills, impalas, antelopes, gazelles, and wild boars, although this time we had no luck with elephants or lions. For the beginner that I was, there was no lack of fallen trunks or dry roots to be confused with live game, which was amusing to those more experienced. It was then that I learned the term "animal tree," a term that I would later entertain myself with at the expense of others who were less experienced than myself.

That afternoon, the third member of the team arrived: Carmen Samuels, a sixty-three year old nurse from Jamaica, with enviable experience in places like Nepal, India, Malawi, and Pakistan.

NOTES

1. Management Sciences for Health (MSH) is based in Boston. MSH has an office in Quito, Ecuador.
2. After graduation from medical school in Ecuador, each doctor owes the country one year of public serv-ice, be it in a city or a rural area, hence the name *Medicina Rural.*

2

FIRST STEPS

SPEAKING OF WORK

My first impression on seeing Mwanza District Hospital was inauspicious. The hospital not only lacked the most indispensable resources but was so oversaturated that we were obliged to accommodate two patients in the same bed and two more below them on the floor. Added to this were concerned family members, resulting in a frightening crowd of people who surely would turn the whole place into an infectious breeding ground. The problem of AIDS presented itself before my eyes with a magnitude that I could hardly have imagined; the tuberculosis ward was in reality a room without hope, the majority of the patients being either HIV positive or already having developed AIDS and dying. Most were young people between twenty and forty years of age for whom life no longer had much to offer. It was difficult for me to accept the fact that this hospital would be the place where I would refer my patients. Africa, it seemed, was a continent in a state of emergency.

ARC did not have a very clear idea of what my functions would be, mostly because we were developing a new program. The material they had sent me in Ecuador was, for the most part, information about what they had done in the Machinga district, which had no relation to the program that was being initiated in the other district, Chikwawa. The origins and details I discovered later: the organization Médecins Sans Frontières (MSF) of France had left the Chikwawa district, and the United Nations High Commissioner for Refugees (UNHCR) requested ARC to take charge of health and sanitation in the district's two camps: Kunyinda and Chang'ambika. During the transitory period UNHCR determined that MSF "would deliver" the two camps to the new organization, which would take charge of them at the beginning of January 1993.

Monday, December 14, 1992, I arrived at Kunyinda refugee camp for the first time. It's difficult to explain what a place like this represents: perhaps the end or the continuation of a life of affliction, where war, destruction, and violence had obliged an individual to leave country, work, and principally friends and family, who perhaps had died during the conflict or who had preferred to face adversity within the boundaries of their own country. Only a civil war of such duration and of such carnage as the one in Mozambique could explain why more than a million of its inhabitants had fled to Malawi. Others had taken refuge in the remaining neighboring countries: South Africa, Tanzania, Zimbabwe, Swaziland, and Zambia.

Kunyinda is located in the lower valley of the Shire River in the south, the country's hottest zone, where temperatures in the summer easily climb over to 110°F (43°C). The first impression I had of the camp was of a large village of huts with straw roofs and adobe walls placed in no apparent order. In front of each house there were no fewer than three children playing, and at the sight of a white man, they threw themselves at the vehicle shouting *mzungu* ("white man"). The population at the time consisted of approximately 60,000 refugees, 8,000 of them children under five years of age, which gives some indication of the fertility rate in this region. The camp was divided into thirteen sections, each with its own leader who tried to keep communities together within each section, the chiefs of each section being the ones with whom, by tradition, each community identifies. Within a total of fifty-seven chiefs, the top one was Chief Chituwi, a respected leader probably in his late fifties, although he looked older, and a character with whom I would have dealings in the future.

Something that never fails to surprise foreigners is the formality with which the Malawi people carry out their simple but difficult lives. They never missed an opportunity to hold a formal meeting, and my arrival was no exception. At the end of the well-known list of petitions, the tribal leaders took advantage of the opportunity to welcome me to the area. It caused great surprise when I addressed them in Portuguese, for, while I was not fluent, it did create a well-disposed ambiance for a future of mutual understanding. Although not everyone there understood, there was no doubt that speaking to them in Portuguese was preferable to speaking in English, a language unknown to Mozambicans and rural Malawians. After the obligatory presentations, I made my first visit to the camp and its health care areas, which included: the Cholera Treatment Unit with an annex for patients with dysentery, the Intensive Nutrition Center, and the Nutritional Clinic—all of them coming under my supervision. Besides that, I visited the Health Care Center and the Maternity and Outpatient Center, which were under the supervision of the Malawi's Ministry of Health.

Médecins Sans Frontières of France had built the previously mentioned cholera units in all the Mozambican refugee camps in Malawi. Kunyinda and Chang'ambika each had a unit, and we inherited both. Constructed of materials typical to the area, that is, indoor and outdoor walls made of reeds and roofs of straw, the cholera units performed a very important function during the rainy season, when the number of cholera cases shot up, sometimes turning into epidemics that affected a whole zone at one time. Health workers ensured that all family members, patients, or health care professionals dipped their feet or their shoes in the little pool of chlorine that blocked each of the two entrances. Within the unit there were three traditional African buildings that served as Observation, Isolation and Rehydration rooms, separated by spaces intended for washing and common areas. Furthermore, there was a pharmacy, where we kept medication and medical instruments. There was also a kitchen. At the height of the epidemic, we came to the point of having up to fifty patients in each room, and when the Shigella dysentery epidemic attacked the region, we fixed up another room to treat those cases, amounting to a total of 200 patients in each unit, or almost 400 in the two camps combined. A patient would be admitted to Observation as soon as the diagnosis was confirmed and the rehydration (given orally or by intravenous infusion) was begun. If the grade of dehydration were moderate or severe, the patient would be transported to the Isolation Room, where treatment would continue and then after two or three days, when the situation abated, to the Rehydration Room, where, before release from the unit, the patient would be given instructions about the preparation of the oral salts as well as a number of packets. The unit personnel was composed almost entirely of local health workers, known as Disease Prevention Workers, or in Portuguese, *Agentes Polivalentes de Enfermedades* (APE's).

The Intensive Nutrition Centers, which MSF also constructed, were single floor buildings divided into three compartments to facilitate the three-phase treatment for malnutrition. It was these centers that provided care and adequate nutrition for the population, especially for infants who were suffering from the consequences of acute or chronic malnutrition, which manifests itself in the form of kwashiorkor or marasmus. The first phase is the introduction to a high-energy content meal, while the second phase is maintenance and the third recuperation. Upon release, children accompanied by their mothers, would continue to return to the Nutritional Clinic once a week, where the medical staff would measure weight by height and upper-arm circumference, follow up on any deviations, distribute a quantity of food for the week, and give nutritional lectures. The staff was composed of nurses and community health personnel who worked in twenty-four shifts. Later on, we were to check the efficiency and effectiveness of these centers, where, by utilizing food rich in energy but at the same time low in cost, numerous cases of pediatric malnutrition were adequately treated. The drought and the later epidemic of dysentery contributed to the drastic increase in the number of cases, which in the first months exceeded 100 children in each Intensive Nutrition Center.

All things considered, one of the main reasons ARC decided to hire me was my experience with the cholera epidemic in Ecuador. Their decision came during the height of the epidemic in Kunyinda, where the unit averaged twenty to thirty admissions daily. I took up my new duties, placing a priority on the standardization of cholera treatment according to the degree of dehydration observed: mild, moderate, or severe with shock. The result within the first few weeks was an evident reduction in the use of Ringer's Lactates,[1] which heretofore they had been administering to every new admission without evaluating the degree of dehydration (twelve to fourteen lactates a patient). After one month we reduced the amount to eight to nine lactates a patient, with the subsequent reduction in treatment cost to ARC.

December 23, 1992

Just hours before Christmas, I referred my first AIDS patient to the N'Gabu Rural Hospital. He was a young man of thirty suffering with persistent chronic diarrhea (resistant to every treatment), cachexia, and decoloration of the hair—this last sign frequently present in black patients with the probable diagnosis of AIDS. He had been admitted with the diagnosis of dysentery, but his condition— after the abdominal pain eased and the bloody diarrhea subsided—did not appear to be improving. In spite of having denied the suspected sexual contacts, one of his brothers admitted to knowing of several visits to the local bordello. The man never returned to the camp. He died weeks after admission.

That same day I had at least the pleasure of seeing the beautiful smiles from children enjoying the little Christmas party that Carmen, the nurse,

17

and I gave the patients in the Intensive Nutrition Center. Carmen brought balloons, which we distributed among the children, and I played some Andean and Ecuadorian music on the charango and the quena.[2] The music reached the young hearts more than any other present. Near the end, the mothers of the patients spontaneously decided to toast us with a beautiful session of traditional song and dance, which was truly a pleasure to watch and to hear. That is the essence of Africa; tragedy and misery go hand in hand with the smile of children at their games, with the joy and rhythm of their songs.

For my first Christmas in Africa, I chose to attend the religious service at the Catholic Church in Liwonde, the town where I would spend the Christmas holidays. Celebration of the mass in this place was a really fascinating experience. The men and women sat apart, each group on either side of the church. The service was in Chichewa and was accompanied by African songs and dances in which all the community participated. The traditional African music combined with religious themes is truly touching; lots of rhythm, while the parishioners' voices split into several tessituras that form an extraordinary chorus. I was the only nonblack person in the whole church, which drew the attention of many eyes for the first few minutes. As the ceremony progressed, I felt embraced by the congregation. I was moved by the spirituality of the moment and said the "Our Father..." in Spanish, while my neighbors said the same prayer in Chichewa, all of us aware that we were saying the same words in two different languages, eager to extend that understanding to other aspects of life.

The Kunyinda camp officially stopped accepting more refugees at the end of 1992, when the number of people already there went over the maximum limit. However, groups of refugees continued to arrive, not only fleeing the violence but also the terrible drought that was affecting the entire region, which had brought on a famine that had already claimed hundreds of lives. The refugees registered in the camp received a card that gave them the right to receive foodstuffs. Those who had not been able to register gathered on a nearby hill that would come to be known as Section 14, although it was not officially recognized. After a few weeks I, together with some of the personnel from ARC, hoping to relieve the situation of those hundreds of "recent arrivals," visited the area, taking along an immunization team from the Ministry of Health. The pathetic picture that met our eyes was frightening: children who had never received any vaccination and demonstrated clear signs of malnutrition; sick people who could not even leave their fragile constructions of branches that served as their shelter; women whose single piece of clothing consisted of tree bark that covered them from the waist down; a high number of cases of trachoma (an ocular condition that can result in blindness); and respiratory and diarrheal diseases in a high percentage of the infant population.

After a long day's work, a large number of children with marasmus and kwashiorkor[3] were referred to the Intensive Nutrition Center in order to correct their caloric and protein deficiencies. Later, we obtained authorization from UNHCR to deliver food rations to the families of the patients admitted to our center. Months later a census of this unprotected population would be authorized to register and to relocate them to another camp in the neighboring district of Mwanza. Some resisted moving from this sector so close to the frontier, preferring to stay on without being registered. For this reason, Section 14 would never be uninhabited, and in the end it became a logistic and sanitary problem.

CHANG'AMBIKA

A few days later I traveled to a second camp in the district of Chikwawa, to Chang'ambika. Located in a hilly area, its greenness and somewhat cooler climate made me feel immediately more comfortable than I had been in the dust, heat, and plain landscape of Kunyinda. The population, although less numerous (22,000 refugees), suffered from the same maladies as those in the other camp, the two camps separated from one another by more than 48 miles (80 kilometers). As for the cholera problem, the unit was completely packed with patients, as was the Dysentery Room. In the weeks ahead a new drama came to life, which ultimately turned into a daily fight against death. In my personal diary, I described some of the first cases:

January 5, 1993.

The claws of death surrounded the Intensive Nutrition Center again, and this time the victim was an orphan child, six months of age, who died in my arms, after our having used up every available resource to save him. The baby had a history of dysentery (diarrhea with blood) for three to four days, and upon examination I found him feverish, with grave dehydration and in shock. The heartbeat was difficult to detect, for which I decided to initiate immediate intravenous therapy. While trying to locate the vein he entered into cardiovascular failure; after having started artificial resuscitation and, as the ultimate resource intracardiac adrenaline, it was not possible to save his short life, one that was in danger from the moment of its inception.

January 8, 1993

It seems that death will surround my work for the rest of the year. This time a girl child, who was admitted in the Intensive Nutrition Center and who was diagnosed as having bacterial pneumonia, died while being transported to the Mwanza Hospital, forty-five minutes after I had decided to refer her to the hospital for showing signs of respiratory failure. While in route, the person who was accompanying the patient did not notice that the mother was giving the comatose child some water to drink. *The vomiting child breathed in the contents, producing death by asphyxiation.*

Reading the diary I can remember even more clearly what happened and the fight that developed within me as I faced a daily average of two to three deaths from the epidemics. A feeling of impotence grew day-by-day, and on occasion I questioned the reason for my presence that seemed barely a patch on a grave injury, which was the reality of the situation with the refugees. When the one who dies is no more than a child, the pain is even more intense, and only the vast amount of ceaseless work even on the weekends kept my mind occupied. Around that time I was alone in the camp since Betty Lee, the seventy-two year old nurse, could not withstand the working conditions, the isolation, and the continual struggle against death, and she canceled her contract and returned to the United States. Instead of falling into desperation, this fact somehow gave me strength to continue, and within a few weeks I was able to write more hopeful lines in my little camp diary.

Now, more than ever, I feel that my work is significant. If it is not humanly possible to do more to save a patient, I know that at least I can bring words of encouragement to the closest relatives, and that although said in a language as remote for them as Spanish, they know the expression of a feeling of solidarity from someone who, in spite of having seen suffering in his own country, has never before seen it in such magnitude.

NOTES

1. Ringer's Lactate is an intravenous solution used to rehydrate a patient diagnosed with severe dehydration, which is a sign of cholera.
2. A *charango* is a small ten string guitar-like Andean instrument; a *quena is* a seven-hole wooden Andean flute.
3. Marasmus and kwashiorkor are types of malnutrition.

3

BECOMING A REFUGEE

THE CIVIL WAR IN MOZAMBIQUE

In order to comprehend the reason why hundreds of thousands of a country's inhabitants feel obliged to flee their towns to take refuge in a foreign country, it is necessary to go back a number of years and to analyze the causes and effects of one of the longest and cruelest civil wars in the history of the African continent.

After finally obtaining independence from Portugal in 1975 and after a long fight against the colonial forces, the Mozambican Liberation Front (FRELIMO) took control, and its leader, Samora Machel, became the first president of Mozambique. In 1976, hostilities began to rise against the then-white minority government of Rhodesia because of the unilateral closing of the common frontier and FRELIMOS's open support of Zimbabwe's nationalist guerrillas. In 1977, FRELIMO declared itself as the Leninist Marxist Party and began to attract military aid from the Soviet Union and from countries in Eastern European bloc. It was then that the Central Intelligence Office of Rhodesia created the National Mozambican Resistance (RENAMO), whose administration was transferred to the Military Intelligence of South Africa a little before the fall of the white government and the creation of the state of Zimbabwe.

RENAMO rapidly generalized the conflict, and, by 1982, the war had arrived in the richest province of Mozambique: Zambezia. From the beginning, cruelty and an unexpected savagery characterized RENAMO's tactics. The multilacerations of ears, noses, lips, and sexual organs of the civilian victims, including children, were as common as the systematic destruction of means of transportation, schools, and hospitals. Massacres and the sacking of entire towns were the keynote of those difficult years. By 1986, RENAMO had control of several rural districts, especially in the province of Tete. At a certain point it was thought the guerrillas would capture the city of Quelimane, thus dividing the country in half and giving RENAMO the opportunity to establish an alternative government. These facts forced tens of thousands of the inhabitants to take refuge in Malawi, initiating the first grand exodus. It was then that the troops from Tanzania and Zimbabwe united to reinforce the FRELIMO government's desperate effort to recapture the lost territories.

In 1987, the forces of the three countries launched an offensive, and RENAMO began to cede its positions; this was a time when the worst massacres of the war occurred, all instigated by RENAMO in a desperate attempt to halt their military reverses. The massive exodus of a civilian population once again began with the search for some personal security in Zimbabwe, Malawi, Tanzania, Zambia, Swaziland, and South Africa. In April 1988, the United States State Department issued a report accusing the rebels of the massacre of at least 100,000 people and of forcing civilians into labor camps. The report also recognized excesses on the part of the government forces, although apparently to a lesser degree.

A military victory seemed more distant as the two factions continued the struggle. At last, the famine of 1991 and 1992, caused by the long drought in the region, forced RENAMO to come to the negotiating table, and, on October 4, 1992, the opposing factions signed a cease-fire in Rome, establishing a timetable of activities to bring about the first democratic elections in the country.

24

THE REFUGEES

The 1951 United Nations Convention defined a refugee as "any person who owing to a well founded fear of being persecuted for reasons of race, religion, nationality, membership of a particular social group or political opinion is outside the country of his nationality and is unable, or owing to fear is unwilling to avail himself of the protection of that country; or who, not having a nationality and being outside the country of his former habitual residence, is unable, or having such fear is unwilling to return to it." In 1969, the Organization of African Unity expanded this definition to include individuals who are fleeing from war situations, civil disturbances, and violence of any type. However, these definitions exclude those who "leave their country to seek economic betterment, as well as persons or groups who may flee their homes for the above or other reasons, yet remain within the borders of their own country."[1] Although Mozambique had a significant internally displaced population, they received little support from the international community for the duration of the conflict.

Up to the signing of the cease-fire, there were a total of two million Mozambican refugees in the six bordering countries: Tanzania, Zambia, Malawi, Zimbabwe, Swaziland, and South Africa. Furthermore, a total of four to five million inhabitants had been displaced internally in zones of less risk within Mozambique. By 1993, there was a total of one million Mozambican refugees in Malawi, distributed in several camps, most of them located close to the common frontier between the two countries. Each refugee camp was divided into several sections or barrios. With the formation of these camps, there were attempts to place the refugees into sections, respecting their ethnic or provincial backgrounds. The leaders of each section were, for the most part, the same leaders or rulers who directed the destinies of the towns before, thus having the objective of making it easier to administer the camp. For each camp, the government of Malawi designated an administrator, who in turn reported to the commissioner of the respective district. With international support the minister of health constructed posts or health centers in each of the camps and furthermore brought in local health personnel who received their pay from the United Nations High Commissioner for Refugees (UNHCR). The non-governmental international organizations (NGOs) were able to carry out their activities in the camp only when they received authorization from the Malawian government, and the activities were coordinated at the district level.

By 1993, the Malawi government was already pressuring UNHCR to speed up the repatriation process for the hundreds of thousands of refugees in the country. The presence of such an elevated number of Mozambicans in Malawi was beginning to create tension in the political and social spheres of that African nation. During the first years of the massive exodus during the mid-80s, Malawi had been viewed as having benefited from the high quantity of resources that the international organizations were mobilizing at that time, which turned out, in part, to have reactivated a rather decayed economy. However, with the passing of years, the negative effects of the presence of more than a million refugees brought about deforestation in vast areas surrounding the refugee camps and an increase in the index of crimes and violence. Moreover, the tension between the Malawian populace in some towns near the camps and the refugees began to grow; they could see that the bulk of international aid was destined for the refugees, while few programs were aimed at supporting the local communities.

This volatile situation had developed gradually. In the beginning the frontier communities had welcome the refugees with whom they shared cultural, linguistic, and familial ties. In the first stage of the exodus, the refugees were assimilated by the Malawian towns along the extensive border shared with Mozambique. Later, when the exodus grew to massive proportions, it became obvious that it was necessary to concentrate the refugees into camps. It was from then on that the difficulties became more evident. The fact that one out of every ten inhabitants of this poor country should find her- or himself a refugee coming from a nation at war creates an extremely difficult situation for the host country if one considers the few resources of that country, in this case Malawi.

The major reported causes of death, in children under the age of five, in refugee-hosting areas in nine Malawi districts by July 1990 were: malaria (25 percent), malnutrition (23 percent), diarrheal diseases (11 percent), measles (10 percent), acute respiratory infections (9 percent), other causes (22 percent). Most of the causes for these deaths are easily preventable by immunization, hygiene and sanitation, and community education. The Centers for Disease Control (CDC) found a strong association between acute protein energy malnutrition and the crude mortality rate among the refugee population, which in the Malawi refugee camps in 1987 reached 1.0 out of 1,000 per month, a rate even less than the corresponding figure for Mozambique in the same year.[2] This reduction does not always occur, because experience from other countries demonstrates that refugees or displaced persons have a higher rate of mortality than those who stay in their own towns, demonstrating the critical situation in Mozambique. That could explain why the influx of refugees continued even after the camps were officially closed. They had a better chance of survival in Malawi.

NOTES
1. *Morbidity and Mortality Weekly Report*, July 24, 1992. Volume 41, No. RR-13.
2. *Ibid.*

4

A NEW HOME

A LITTLE OF THE DAILY LIFE IN MALAWI

Although I did not know it yet, Chang'ambika would truly become my home. For reasons of security, representatives of international organizations were prohibited from living within the refugee camps. Medecins Sans Frontieres had partially reconstructed a house in N'Gona, a rural town only 6 miles (10 kilometers) from the camp. This small but typical African village contained thirty to fifty huts made of clay and straw. The largest structures were the health center and the "ARC house," as it came to be known. To get there, one takes the dirt road that originates in Mwanza, the capital of the district of the same name, some twenty-seven miles (forty-five kilometers) away, and crosses the Thambani Forest Reserve. The Gaga River divides the village in half and provides all the water for the residents' needs; in a dry spell the people are obliged to dig into the river bottom in order to obtain the vital liquid. The closest well is quite far away in a neighboring village some nine miles (fifteen kilometers) away.

In N'Gona, there is no particular order in the placement of the living quarters, which are located for the most part along the length of the road that continues toward the Mozambican frontier and the refugee camp. At times people and animals alike share the same roof. The women, especially, are dedicated to their daily tasks: to gathering firewood and water and to planting, harvesting, and grinding corn in order to obtain the flour they use to prepare the ever-present *n'zima*, a kind of cooked corn dough that the Malawians eat everyday with pumpkin leaves, peanuts, tomatoes and, when available, goat meat. Every family has a garden located generally on the outskirts of the village, where they cultivate primarily corn and beans. Those few who are a little better off also have goatherds and one or two milking cows.

"Gaga House," as our residence was known, truly represented Malawi and the conditions in which the majority of the population lives. There was no electricity, hardly any potable water, and no sewage system. We transported water in great tanks from the camp, where it was manually pumped from wells. The water destined for human consumption was placed in filtered tanks especially located within the house. In the eyes of our neighbors, this house was the most luxurious and comfortable of all in the village. It had a living room, three little bedrooms, a storeroom, and an extension of bamboo and brick, where we had our kitchen-dining room. Furthermore, we had a refrigerator that functioned with paraffin (later we got a fridge that functioned with gas), two filtered tanks for drinking water, and a gas stove, among other items. There was a latrine in the back part of the house and a rustic shower fed from an aluminum tank that had to be filled periodically. The thing that was the most difficult for me to accustom myself to was the latrine, which had not received any maintenance for months and, moreover, where there were numerous, disagreeable cockroaches, most of them housed in the hole of the latrine. The huts around the house made quite a contrast with their adobe walls and thatched straw roofs. Only a few families owned a latrine, which in most cases was not well maintained.

In spite of everything, our house had its charms, and it felt like my real home with candlelight dinners every night, unequaled feelings of peace and independence that were interrupted only on occasion by the village children's songs and traditional games (usually on moonless, dark nights) and by the African drums celebrating some special occasion. I learned to value the gift that in our society has become an article of luxury—silence. The sounds of nature were the only ones that broke that precious calm. They occurred in such a way that they were absorbed by the ambiance, an atmosphere of peace and tranquillity. The staff who worked for us was comprised of locals: the cook, Pedro, who also did other domestic tasks for us; and two guards, Robert and Mateya. Of the three, the only one who spoke a little English was Robert. With the other two I was obliged to use some Chichewa—a language that I would only learn in its most basic form—and the universal language of signs mixed with English simple words. Pacha, the cat that we inherited from MSF, lived on insects exclusively, although upon our arrival his diet was complemented with products from our pantry. It is appropriate to mention here that Pedro was not a culinary chef, and for one or two months the daily menu never varied from rice and beans. Later, he lost some of his timidity and tried different dishes that were easy to prepare like spaghetti and soups from leftovers. However, the rice and beans were never absent from our table more than twice a week. It was very difficult to get meat, so our diet was, for the most part, vegetarian.

My second residence was located fourteen miles (twenty-three kilometers) from the Kunyinda camp, in a village of some importance in the district: N'Gabu. From there, it took from twenty-five to sixty minutes by vehicle to arrive at the camp, depending on the road conditions, which alternated according to the season. The house in N'Gabu was located in a residential area of "lower population density" reserved for middle-class civil servants only, most of them of course belonged to the MCP (Malawi Congress Party). N'Gabu, in spite of being a tiny village, was linked to Blantyre by an asphalt highway, although the road was filled with potholes in its last stretches. It had a district hospital, houses of adobe and cement—some with gardens, some local businesses, a police station, and public services of drinking water, lights, sewers—and even telephone lines. The house itself had all the services and comforts, including potable water (although from time to time it stopped running), electric lights, sewer, a toilet, a shower, a sink, and a telephone. In the back part we had a garden and a little plot of vegetables.

As one would expect, this second residence came with the time-honored personnel whom ARC had contracted to perform the household duties: a cook, Robert, and three guards who took shifts twenty-four hours a day. Carmen Samuels, the nurse, and John Newohner, the sanitation engineer lived in this house. One bedroom was designated for my use while I was at the Kunyinda camp.

COMPANIONS AT WORK

To describe my two work and living companions is not an easy job, but it is an interesting one. While Carmen Samuels and Betty Lee shared certain similarities, they were still very different. Among their similarities is their vast experience in public health in developing countries, their desire to help those in need, their ability to take on the aura of giving and sacrifice that surrounded them and, lastly, their ages, both were past sixty-years-old.

Carmen Samuels, with a much stronger personality than her counterpart, was given, at times, to passionate outbursts in monologues that progressively increased in intensity until they approached a fury, all this due to her passion for service and to the terrible pressures of work that we all felt during those first three months. Carmen took on the Nutrition Center at Kunyinda as her personal crusade and the children as her protégés. On occasion she could become so involved with the refugee drama that in a thoughtless moment all her hidden frustration would burst forth upon the nearest person. She was also more the housekeeper who took pleasure in having everything clean and in its place. She preferred to wash the dishes after dinner rather than wait for the cook, who would have done them the following morning.

Betty Lee was very determined in her work, but she lacked Carmen's training and clinical experience as nurse practitioner.[1] She is of the old school who believe that a doctor is the only one who can make decisions and that a nurse is there only to help carry them out. It was always difficult for her to act independently, and whenever I traveled to the other camp she would become very anxious, so I ended up spending sixty percent of my time in Chang'ambika. On the other hand, Betty was much less meticulous about aspects such as cleanliness, decorating, etc. To sum up, the result was that it was much more agreeable to live with Betty, but more interesting and productive to work with Carmen, who did not need constant supervision and always took the initiative during my absence. By March 1993, Betty's resistance to living in Chang'ambika's semi-isolation, plus the arduous work and sacrifice, reached its limitations, and she quit for reasons of stress and exhaustion. Mrs. Lee submitted her resignation, which I accepted as soon as she asked my opinion. The workload doubled, but I reorganized the local personnel to cover her absence, and then we waited for a new expatriate nurse.

POLITICAL AND THE SOCIAL ISSUES IN MALAWI

It is interesting to find oneself immersed in a world divided into two colors, white and black. The country has a small but powerful white community, most of them originating from South Africa, Zimbabwe, Great Britain, Holland, United States, and some few born in Malawi to whom the Banda government has not given Malawi citizenship for their being white. Most are found fulfilling short- or medium-term contracts with international organizations, acting as professors or technical advisors, or as consultants or executives in government offices.

The South African influence is evident in every aspect of daily life in Malawi. The few supermarkets in the principal cities have a limited variety of products, and what few there are invariably come from South Africa. The same is true of magazines, household articles, sports equipment, etc. There is very important commercial and tourist exchange between the two countries, explained partially by the fact that until 1994 Malawi was one of the few African countries for which the white South African could obtain a visa, this because of apartheid, the racial segregation policy that the long-standing government maintained during the decades of white supremacy and also because of South Africa's political and financial interests in its neighbor.

Following the political theme in Malawi at the beginning of 1993, the then president for life, Ngazu Dr. Kamuzu Banda, finally gave his consent to holding a referendum in which the public had a voice about the possibility of turning Malawi into a multiparty country. Up to that time, the only political party legally allowed was the Malawi Congress Party (MCP), whose leader was the same Dr. Banda. It seems the nonagenarian president (then ninety-two years old) finally gave in to external pressures and polite warnings regarding foreign aid—so vital to the country—and he acceded to carrying out a referendum in March 1993. At the beginning of February, I had the almost historic opportunity of seeing the president in what would be one of his last visits to the districts. It was enlightening to observe the caravan that accompanied him and prepared for his reception. Hours earlier, the police and members of the MCP forced the proprietors of Blantyre's stores and business to close their doors in order to go out to salute the *Ngwasi* (the "chosen one"). Students from grade schools and high schools were practically forced to leave the classrooms and to stand on the streets for long hours to show their "support" for the dictator. Women wearing dresses and/or uniforms printed with the image of Banda were lined up along the downtown streets of Blantyre to await the passing procession.

When the motorized caravan finally passed by (there were no fewer than ten Mercedes Benz cars, fifteen to twenty motorcycles, and five trucks filled with soldiers), the people's answer was clear: Only those who obviously belonged to the MCP or those who were in the pay of the Party cheered and applauded the passing caravan. The rest of the population held itself in expectant silence, although there was an occasional shout of dissidence, which, only a few months earlier, would have been inconceivable for fear of reprisals. This time, Kamuzu Banda was traveling in a red Rolls Royce limousine convertible with white leather seats. Dressed in an immaculate dark suit of English cut and with a matching English hat, he held in his right hand something that from afar looked like some species of conductor's baton, but as the car came closer, I could see that we were dealing with a scepter from which the hair of some animal was hanging and which Banda was continually shaking as he passed by. Later, I found out that the hair came from the tail of a lion, which, when agitated, took the role of "shaking off bad spirits," according to tradition. Another popular belief says that Banda has two guardian lions that usually accompany him wherever he goes, and that these invisible beasts are easily controlled by their master through the use of the famous scepter. On one occasion there were articles published in the local newspapers about the supposed witchery of activists belonging to the governing party. The matter came to the point of involving even the higher government spheres, and during a massive gathering in the Kamuzu Stadium in Blantyre, Banda, while giving one of his hackneyed orations, very seriously warned those witches who were performing "exorcisms against my people," that they must suspend these spells immediately, and that they should remember that he not only was the leader of the nation but also "the number one and the most powerful sorcerer" of all. From this it should be no surprise that the image of Banda grew to one of mystery with supernatural powers, all of which served him in governing a superstitious people.

Under the Banda regime, the government was in total control of the press. Only the president and his party (the MCP) were allowed to publish newspapers, and the Malawi Broadcasting Corporation (MBC), the only broadcasting media in the country, was a mouthpiece of the MCP government. The Censorship and Control of Entertainments Act was passed in 1968, creating the Malawi Censorship Board to control publications that circulate in Malawi. In only the first seven years of its existence, the board banned 840 books, more than 100 periodicals and 16 films. Since then the list has expanded considerably. The banned publications range from the political (Marx, Engels), through the sexual (*Playboy* magazine, the Kama Sutra) to works of literature, including authors such as Ernest Hemingway, Graham Greene, and Emile Zola.

A LITTLE ABOUT SOCCER

With the arrival of John Newohner, the sanitation and environmental engineer, the ARC work force for the Chikwawa district was complete. His responsibilities included the overall supervision of sanitation activities, such as well and latrine construction and maintenance, water supply and chlorination, and the logistics of the camps. Among other (his) qualities, John liked sports, and among those was soccer. From this interest, the idea began to germinate to organize a soccer championship, first in Chang'ambika and later in Kunyinda. Permanently based at the Kunyinda camp, John was in charge of organizing the tournament there, and I did the same in Chang'ambika. Broad segments of the community became very enthusiastic about the idea, so much so that it prompted a meeting of the camp chiefs where they addressed this and other subjects. Later, I received a letter from the social worker that indicated that the Kunyinda chiefs were mobilizing the community there to fix up the soccer field, which had fallen into deplorable disrepair. The number of people who participated was so large and so motivated that the field was completely ready in less than six hours. For its part, ARC contributed the soccer goals, the nets, and the uniforms.

I think I should describe how important soccer is in these latitudes. It is the most practiced sport in the country and possibly on the entire continent. The fact that no large infrastructure is needed helps to explain the well-earned popularity of the "king of sports" on a continent as poor as much of Africa is. I was always surprised to see the ingenuity the African children used to fabricate their own balls, that is, utilizing empty plastic milk bottles, and more surprising was the fact that these improvised balls even bounced. A cleared field, in many cases not completely level and usually filled with holes, three rustic sticks on each end for goal posts, and, finally, a group of enthusiastic kids was all that was needed to practice this popular sport. Those players who had shoes—of whatever type—were considered very fortunate since the great majority were barefooted.

The games between the different villages were reason enough for a fiesta or social gathering. The visiting team, accompanied by its followers, walked to the meeting place, at times after having covered long distances of many hours' duration. In the village where the game was to take place they were received by a little committee that brought drinks and showed them where they would lodge. After a short rest they were led to the field where they started warming up. Among the supporters for each team were women who cheered on their respective teams with traditional songs and dances. There was always a witch who hung around the rival goal post in order to intervene with his incantations, which he made on repeated occasions, so that his team would score, helped by his spells. The technique left much to be desired, since everyone ran behind the ball without any great tactical plan. However, it's worthwhile to emphasize that certain players did have excellent qualities; strength and good physical condition were common denominators among practically all the players that I saw compete in the different villages where we traveled with the team on some weekends. At the end of the encounter, no matter the result of the game, the visitors would be honored with a dinner, and if they came from very far away, they would be provided with lodgings until the next day when they began their return.

Almost every afternoon, at the conclusion of the day's work, I watched the local Chang'ambika team's daily soccer practice. I almost always wound up playing. Before the first game against the team from the neighboring village, we organized a *minga*[2] to enhance playing field conditions. The players as well as the children leant their support. It was then that I realized the children had no fitting activity to keep them busy after school. They could not play soccer since they had no ball, and when the team was playing they were immediately thrown off the field. I spoke with the team captain, George, and I proposed my plan to him, to create a soccer school for children from eight to fifteen years of age. He looked pleased when I promised that I would personally pay the salary and the expenses for directing and training the children. Within only a few days approximately twenty-five children began to practice.

NOTES

1. A nurse practitioner can make complete physical examinations, diagnose a number of common illnesses, and prescribe some medication without consulting of doctor.
2. *Minga* is the traditional, volunteer community work carried out throughout the Andean region since prehispanic times.

5

HEALTH ISSUES

NEW EPIDEMICS

A normal workday began with the rounds to the Intensive
Nutrition Center (INC) and to the cholera camp. Because
of the number of admissions, it took the whole morning to
complete these rounds. Stanley Banda and I always spent
at least half an hour discussing issues related to logistics
or sanitation as well as trying to solve the innumerable
problems that emerged day after day. In the afternoon, I
accompanied the health teams in their visits to the different sections, which included nutrition follow-up, immunization, and home visits. This direct contact with the
refugees allowed me to expand my vocabulary in
Chichewa, which slowly began to grow.

From the end of January onward, the number of cases
of acute respiratory infections (ARI) began to swell, principally in children. At the beginning of February, five children died from ARI (14 percent of the registered deaths),
and eight more deaths came at the end of the month (45
percent of all the deaths in this month). Morbidity[1] rose
from forty-six cases of ARI (1.7 percent of all the diagnosed cases) to seventy-five cases (3 percent) in the same
period. The crowded living conditions in the INC as well
as the still inadequate sanitary conditions in certain parts
of the camp seemed to be the principal causes of this new

epidemic. It was very difficult to accept that a new adversity was hovering over these people. During the cholera and dysentery outbreaks our personnel was overloaded with work, and now it was necessary to mobilize our last resources to avoid having this new problem expand even more.

Not having an isolation unit for these patients at our disposal nor adequate health personnel who knew how to manage a patient with ARI, I decided to open a special unit in a little empty room at the front of the Maternity House at Chang'ambika. I altered the shifts for several of the health technicians so that they could move to the new unit, and I organized a plan for on-the-job training where they could learn correct management treatment for an ARI patient. During the first weeks my supervision was necessarily exacting, but as the staff gained confidence, I was slowly able to let go and delegate responsibilities. Despite that, only the nurse or myself could prescribe antibiotics. In the following month we registered only one death from pneumonia, in spite of the fact that morbidity from respiratory infections continued to rise to ninety-one cases (3.3 percent of all the diagnosed pathologies). At the end of April 1993, there were no deaths reported, and the number of cases progressively began to diminish. While we were controlling these outbreaks, we never stopped diagnosing, treating, or referring many diseases of less frequency but of equal or more gravity, such as bacterial meningitis, cerebral malaria, renal insufficiency, congestive heart failure, and AIDS. In January, an outbreak of bacterial conjunctivitis broke out in the INC centers of both camps and attacked seventeen (41 percent) of the children admitted to the center in Chang'ambika and forty-four (31 percent) of the patients in Kunyinda. It was necessary to initiate adequate treatment to those cases and prophylaxis to all the new patients being admitted to the unit. In the two months following, this problem—at least temporarily—disappeared.

Diseases such as respiratory infections, acute diarrheal diseases, and malnutrition were always present. To eradicate them, it would be necessary to provide access to water and sanitation, good nutrition, hygiene, immu-

nization coverage, and perhaps more importantly, understanding from the national and local authorities on the
importance of health as a mean and goal for economic
development. The inclusion of new actors from the private and public sectors could bring a new dimension to the
delivery of health care in which social participation
becomes a major tool to empower the people. However, in
order to get involved, the population at large must comprehend that health is not merely the absence of disease.
There is a more comprehensive approach to health that
includes a variety of determinants within the social, economic, and cultural domains.

LABOR PROBLEMS

My relationship with the personnel in both camps always
went along very well and with a mark of mutual respect.
We did not lack for problems, but we always maintained
a rather suitable working atmosphere. However, the first
true labor crisis presented itself shortly after my arrival.
The problem came up during January's salary payments
to Chang'ambika's personnel. MFS had recognized a
Christmas bonus for the month of December, but the
workers thought that it meant a continued salary increase
for the following months. Upon assuming control of the
camps, the ARC maintained the salaries based on those
of MSF, which the United Nations High Commissioner
for Refugees (UNHCR) had established.

The out-of-place shouting and the threats to suspend
daily work—which in fact already had been suspended—
called for my attention. Within a few minutes, Stanley
Banda, the public health advisor, brought me up to date
on the situation and immediately directed me to the place
where approximately sixty Mozambican workers had
gathered. It is interesting to observe that certain individuals behaved rather timidly alone, but upon joining a
protest group, their attitude changed radically to the point
of becoming aggressive. However, it seemed that my presence somewhat calmed their burning emotions and the
silence I was able to achieve allowed enough time for me
to speak without interruption. Have no doubt that it was

difficult to convince them of the nature of the higher increment in December, and I promised them to make a revision in salaries that would be just and, if the UNHCR authorized it, would go into effect immediately. At that moment divided criterions arose to which I proceeded to give individual audience, calling several known faces by first names and asking them for understanding. Some of them were parents of patients at the center, and that contributed to my increased credibility. In the end, they decided to wait for the aforementioned revision and to return to their daily labors.

For the month of March, a twenty-five percent increase was approved, which the workers received with signs of enthusiasm. In truth, the salary for these people was so small that this raise was well justified. However, we made it very clear that, except for bonuses and other benefits, this would be the last salary increase for the year, such a declaration being necessary to avoid a series of strikes.

Earlier, I mentioned a man who would become a key member of my team in the next months, Stanley Banda. He graduated with honors from the University of Malawi, where he became a certified health technician. Together, with Alfred Mahone—a fellow technician who graduated in the same class—both young professionals took jobs with ARC as soon as they graduated from the university and became the public health advisors for each of the two camps in the Chikwawa district. The demand for this type of health professional was so high that NGOs and government officials were ready to hire the fifteen to twenty students who graduated each year. Along with his wife and two children, Banda moved to Chang'ambika, where he rented a small house within the camp limits. Immediately, Stanley took over some of the time-consuming administrative work, as well as the sanitation component of the program, taking into consideration that John Newohner was based in Kunyinda and rarely came to Chang'ambika. Banda's good nature, manners, and hard-working habits brought him as many friends as his honesty attracted a few enemies. Skinny, wide-eyed, and wearing a moustache that brought contrast to his otherwise childlike face, Stanley irradiated energy wherever he went, and I never remember hearing a complaint from him about the amount of work, except once, just before the health fair, a major event that I will discuss later.

Stanley Banda, as everyone else, soon learned that life in a refugee camp was difficult and in some ways even dangerous. The following is the account of the incident that forced Stanley to move out of the camp.

March 1993

Stanley had not yet been able to identify the workers who were stealing from the storage room. However, he let all the workers know that he was aware of the problem and would continue the investigation until he discovered those who were behind it. A few days after I received his report, which included a list of the lost items, Stanley received an anonymous hand-written letter. He came to me with the letter written in Chichewa and told me that this was the second one he had received, but he did not give the first much thought until the second one had arrived. Considering the number of concealed weapons in the area, and the number of excombatants from both factions who were used to killing, any death threat had to be seriously considered. ARC in Blantyre agreed that Banda had to move out of the camp. They were also concerned for my safety, so they made sure I was not left alone for a second in the camp, and as soon as it got dark I had to be out of the camp. It was not a pleasant way to work, so we went back to the infamous letter and tried to identify the handwriting. We looked in the registry book where the workers signed their names, or put their fingerprint—if they were illiterate—after receiving their salary, and found a few names written in a similar style. Then, we went through hundreds of job-searching letters and discarded most of them. We finally came up with three samples of handwriting that looked very much like the one in the letter and submitted them to the local police. Two of the men had worked for MSF and had moved back to Mozambique some time ago. The third man was still working for us, and, coincidentally, he had access to the storage room. This was our man! He was taken to the police station, where they learned that he was already living across the border in Kapiridsanje, and that he kept not one but several ration cards for food distribution. That was sufficient reason to fire him. The police told him not to return to Chang'ambika or he would be jailed. Stanley did not receive any more letters, and we never saw the man again.

Stanley Banda would become my right hand man and the person in charge of the ARC overall supervision whenever I was absent.

MYSTERIOUS AFRICA

Moving forward in the adaptation process, I continued to learn new aspects of the culture and traditions of the people of central Africa, more specifically, about the Chewa and Yao ethnic groups. The traditions and customs of this part of the continent, as in many other countries, are transmitted orally to new generations. Some have fallen into disuse, but there are others that refuse to disappear in spite of this being an era of advancement and technology.

The value of the extended family was made evident to me on more than one occasion. Malawians call their uncles "father" and their aunts "mother," so that it was difficult to know when the workers were asking for permission to see their parents or only their uncles. I was told in advance that I should limit the funeral leaves to a maximum of three a year, otherwise they would attend every single funeral in their village ("brothers" and "cousins" could be just anybody in the village). In reference to death, in certain parts of Malawi (in the Lower Shire), where the Chewa and Yao groups live, after a funeral and the three-day period of lamentations, it is acceptable that the oldest brother of the deceased has sexual relations with the widow. This brother must assume the care for raising his orphaned nephews and nieces until they reach the age of majority; therefore, by assuming the responsibility of the father, he also assumes the rights of the husband, even if it is for a limited time, in most cases to the period immediately following the funeral, which can last several days. The brother, then returns to his own wife. This demonstration of frivolity is a sign of consent for the invited mourners to resume their daily life—including their sexual practices—without fear of offending the deceased or his kinsmen.

The foreign religious trends that penetrated Africa at the end of the eighteenth century have left their footprint on all the regions of Malawi. Christianity represents the majority (65 percent), followed by a large Muslim population (16 percent), and the so-called Animists (19 percent), the latter following a traditional religion based on ancestral beliefs. In the region of the Lower Shire, there is a religious sect, self-named Christian Baptists, that permits and, according to some, even promotes polygamy among its followers. This cult has created problems for the medical profession. Since they do not allow their members to receive any medication—including vaccines, prenatal care, and most of all blood transfusions—they are more exposed to innumerable complications. In one case, the father of a patient in the INC, a follower of this sect, refused an intravenous injection for his son, and so the child died of dehydration.

It came to mind one dark night in N'Gona, as I lay under a mantel of hundreds of stars in the sky and while the incessant beating of drums celebrating some occasion broke the placid but at times tumultuous way of life in these latitudes. That day, in particular, had been extremely hot. During the night the children of N'Gona played and sang for several hours under the moonless sky. Their games, similar to our children's rounds, were sung in the local Chewa dialect. The melodies were of an enviable beat and rhythm that allowed easy memorization of the tune, if not so much the words that ran along at a speed impossible to follow. The distant drumbeats accompanied the children's games almost all the time, and I fell asleep lulled by the mystical sounds. African drums are the pulse of the heart that nourishes all the continent, and with them they mark the hour of births, marriages, and deaths. During the first few weeks it was impossible for me to concentrate while the drums were sounding in the distance. Little by little they became an unceasing part of the nocturnal sound, and later I came to miss their beating, a cry that evokes the vitality of this continent.

The process of tuning a drum was something that never ceased to amaze me: the percussionist lights a fire in the area where a dance ceremony will be performed. The hollow part of the wood of the drum is placed toward the flames, so that the heat expands the animal skin to the desired pitch. At the same time, the drummer applies a type of grease to the exterior and later to the interior surface of the drum to ensure that the heat evenly distributes itself throughout the entire surface. When this procedure is finished, the ceremony begins.

It is then that one takes in the true Africa, that which exists only outside the cities, that of intoxicating rhythm and dance, that of the simple life and also that of cruel drama. It seemed that a strange alliance was beginning to blossom between this Ecuadorian and the magical continent. The rosy tones of the evenings bid farewell to the light of the day only to give way to a night of clear sky scattered with constellations impossible to see in other regions. At this time the pure air turned into the refreshing breeze that drew a person out of the house in order to forget the hot hours of the midday sun and to give in to already forgotten dreams that take one to magic places. Often it was difficult to believe that I truly was in this forgotten village in a little African country, whose name would mean nothing to most people in other places. On those occasions I took a deep breath and tried to capture the air surrounding me, so that I could keep it in my lungs forever. My eyes were striving to take in the indescribable landscapes and imperishable images that would last in my memory forever. My hands wanted to capture particles of space surrounding me in order to transform them into today's recollections. My voice left its imprint on the infinite as a sign of an ephemeral presence in that microcosm. Africa was beginning to open doors that I did not know I possessed, gates that I had kept locked for a long time, for I did not have the key, nor the willingness to step into the unknown. I had come to discover a continent, but it was Africa that was discovering me.

A NEW VICTIM OF "BAD AIR"

> *One day of fever takes away a year's worth of good health.*
> —Swahili proverb

March 23, 1993

That day transpired more slowly than usual. The work seemed exhausting, and all the while it was taking more and more strength to maintain my concentration. Days earlier I had begun to suffer the ill effects of hard work and stress complicated by a strep throat and gastrointestinal distress, but the great number of patients in the Nutrition Center as well as in the Cholera Unit didn't allow me any rest. This time, however, by the end of the day I was exhausted and without the pep to do absolutely anything. At first, I attributed it to the intensity of the day in the camp and, given the amount of work and tension, I thought that a good rest would end my ills.

The next morning I felt somewhat recuperated, and I proceeded to go on to Blantyre to participate in a working meeting. Toward the end of the meeting the earlier-mentioned symptoms returned even stronger, and I was beginning to feel feverish. I started to return to the camp, but, upon arriving at Mwanza, I asked the chauffeur to buy some aspirin, after which we continued on our way toward Chang'ambika. Arriving at N'Gona, it was evident that my fever was high, and I began to have chills and to go into a general decline. By then the diagnosis was evident: "paludism" or, as it is known in this part of the world, malaria (bad air). This ill-

*ness, considered the principal cause of mortality
and morbidity in Malawi and in sub-Saharan
Africa, was claiming another victim.*

Malaria, a feverish and debilitating disease caused by the
Plasmodium parasite, is contracted through the bite of
the *Anopheles* mosquito. The type of malaria most common in Malawi is caused by the *Plasmodium falciparum*
which, in turn, is more serious and can bring death to the
patient. It is difficult to comprehend the magnitude of
this public health problem. Upon examining statistical
data, one finds that only in Chang'ambika did the monthly
number of cases fluctuate; from 1,000 to 2,000 (in a population of 15,000 to 20,000 inhabitants), diminishing
somewhat in the dry season. Innumerable workdays were
lost, and the socioeconomic costs were impossible to deci-
pher. In January 1993, 2,045 cases of malaria were
reported in Chang'ambika alone (76 percent of all the
diagnosed cases), of which 965 were older than five and of
those, approximately 600 were economically active adults
(28 percent of the total number of cases). With an average
of two days in bed or at rest, this represents 1,200 lost
workdays, without counting the days of leave granted for
the purpose of caring for small children affected by this illness. On average, each individual suffered two attacks of
malaria a year, bringing the figure up to 2,400 lost workdays a year. Death from malaria was seldom reported,
but they were never fewer than three to five fatalities a
month, on average, in each of the two camps.

May 1993

*That night was the first in which reality was slowly
leaving me, giving way to strange periods of hal-
lucination. From then on a heavy sweat took hold
of me, day and night, leaving me only a few
moments of lucidity, for which, with great effort, I
took the opportunity to leave my imprisoning bed—
at least for a few minutes. A parade of images
crossed my mind in a delirious dream in which I
couldn't distinguish human from animal, actual*

from fictitious, real from unreal. The absence of the human voice and company exacerbated the loneliness that at that time was filled with fantastic beings that saturated my mind with unintelligible dialogues that completely engrossed me, as I discovered later.

I took advantage of one of those moments of lucidity to take two tablets of the antimalarial medicine Fansidar® (Sulphametidin Pyrimethamine) and Paracetamol to reduce my fever. The second night was much longer and more painful than the first, for the sickness had reached its peak. During the chills I had perspired profusely and was in a state of semiconsciousness that should have worried the guards who had seen very little of me in the last twenty-four hours. I often awoke bathed in a sweat and with such extreme weakness that the mere fact of raising myself to go to the latrine turned into a feat. On the morning of the third day, my condition was obviously deteriorating, and it seemed that the Fansidar was slow to take effect, or it was still to take effect, or—due to the acuteness of the attack—it was not going to take effect at all.

It was good fortune that the guards and Pedro, the cook, alarmed by my state of health, decided to call the chauffeur who lived some 400 meters from the house. Francis rushed over and with everyone's help I was put in the back seat of ARC's Toyota Land Cruiser, and this was the last I remember. Later I found out that during the journey to the Malamulo Adventist Hospital in Blantyre, I was delirious and raving in a loud voice, and that at last I had fallen into a state of perspiration that did not leave until after I was in the hospital. I awoke in the room with an acute ringing in my ears and an intravenous infusion of saline solution in my right arm that was dripping one of the most potent antimalarial medicines of the day—quinine.[2]

Due to the high resistance of the parasite to a number of ever-increasing antimalarial drugs (Chloroquine, Fansidar, etc.), the related quinine is reserved for those cases that are most severe, hoping to ensure an effective result. At the root of this episode was the fact that it worried me more to use the preventative prophylactic therapy, Mefloquine, a medicine that came to us from the United States, and that we were to take every week. Unfortunately, after a few months, the secondary effects of this drug became intolerable: palpitations, terrible nightmares, a rise in blood pressure, and then depression. I had to dispense with this medication.

At times I think that episode of malaria was an initiation rite, the threshold that differentiated between my being merely a visitor and one who truly wanted to live on the continent and to take part in its daily life, becoming, it is hoped, a catalyst for small or perhaps great changes. In many cases, it is necessary to undergo certain experiences for oneself in order to understand the true magnitude of the daily drama of the average citizen better.

NOTES

1. Morbidity refers to the proportionate number of individuals who are sick from a determined pathology within a determined population and time.
2. Intense headache, accompanied by tinnitus (buzzing in the ears) and vertigo are among the secondary effects of quinine (see *Physician's Desk Reference*: 1992.)

6

THE ADVENTURE OF LIVING

FIRST FLASH VISIT TO MOZAMBIQUE

April 1993

A little before noon one Sunday, as I was returning from the Chang'ambika camp, it occurred to me to take that mysterious highway that, according to what I'd been told, ran to the Mozambican frontier. On more than one occasion during the rainy season, we had found ourselves completely isolated because of the atrocious conditions of the only road in the Malawian territory that connected us with Mwanza. The increase in the number of patients in grave condition who needed immediate referral to the District Hospital of Mwanza frequently forced us to use this third-class road, and the consequences of turning around or suspending a trip were often fatal. The search for an alternate route to Mwanza via Mozambique became a priority; it would eliminate our complete dependency upon the one route, and, being much shorter, we would gain valuable time. Also, in case of political violence or some other eventuality in Malawi, it would offer an alternative evacuation toward the city of Tete in Mozambique.

With the little information I gleaned from those who made the journey by foot, I began the trip quite confident that it would not last very long. My original idea was simply to locate this road and return to the camp. For the first few miles, the dirt road was no different from others. Then the rural border police station came into sight and I stopped. The guard on duty did not bother to ask many questions, and I continued toward the invisible border. After climbing a small hill, I drove onto an asphalt road: I was in Mozambique. I truly felt like the shipwrecked sailor who, thought for months that he was the only living soul on the island, then decided to cross the island only to find a five-star hotel on the opposite side. However, I still needed to know how long it would take to get to Mwanza from this side. After having doubts about which direction to take, I decided to follow a northeasterly course and went on my way for approximately twenty minutes without meeting even one other vehicle. My objective was to get to Zobue, a frontier town on the Mozambican side, to ascertain whether the distance to Mwanza would be much shorter taking this road.

The cease-fire between the RENAMO guerrillas and the FRELIMO government forces had been signed only a few months earlier, and there were still skirmishes and breakdowns in the truce, especially in the frontier regions. My mind began to imagine the worst: mines at the turn of the road, a column of guerrillas sent out to intercept my passage, a stray bullet.... After a little while, I saw in the distance a white armored vehicle that was coming from the opposite direction; only its color prevented me from turning around and making a hasty retreat. At closer inspection, I was able to confirm, to my relief, that I was dealing with a column of armored vehicles from ONUMOZ, the United Nations peace force that was patrolling the zone to prevent confrontations and to maintain the cease-fire. This particular column was comprised of Botswanian soldiers who cheerfully greeted me in passing. I believe they must have thought that I was a functionary of United Nations because of the kind of vehicle I was driving and because it was white and had blue insignias similar to those of UN vehicles.

As I was nearing my destination, I decided to turn around, for I had just realized that I'd brought none of my personal papers with me, and the closer I came to the frontier the greater the possibility someone would demand some identification from me. However, the point of the trip was carried out, since I had proven that taking this route saved at least twenty minutes, time that, in case of a medical emergency, could mean the difference between life and death.

The following day, by sheer coincidence, we had a very interesting visitor. Chipembere (Rhinoceros) is the battle name of the RENAMO's commander who was visiting the Chang'ambika refugee camp that day. I should mention that his name was given to him for his bravery in combat. As soon as I heard of his visit, I sent messengers to ask if I could converse with him. After his agreeing to meet with me, we had an interview that lasted more than an hour, during which we covered aspects of mutual interest. Specifically, I wanted his word that there would be no interference with our vehicles traveling the asphalt road that ran through Mozambique and RENAMO's territory. I indicated that those vehicles would be taking patients from the refugee camp to Mwanza. Chipembere accepted our proposal without hesitation and, for his part, asked that we study the possibility of extending our health programs to Kapiridsanje, the zone the U.N. has designated for the refugee repatriation process immediately following the cease fire. Before leaving, the commander offered to send me the gift of a chicken once a month as a show of good will.

According to the instructions of my translator, my refusal would have been a personal insult, so I gladly accepted.

WORKING IN A REFUGEE CAMP

By the beginning of March, the health teams of both camps were better organized. We had two training seminars for the local health personnel that focused on the correct management of cholera patients as well as patients with acute respiratory infections. Also, the patient referral system was working better, the ordering and delivery of medical supplies was proceeding regularly, and our relationship with the health personnel working for the Ministry of Health (MOH) health center was one of mutual collaboration. As for the health aspect, the program to chlorinate the water was also going along rather well, while the rate of construction of latrines was on the rise. For water chlorinization—a fundamental aspect in any program for prevention of cholera and other acute diarrheal diseases—we organized a system by which the local health promoters each took on eight-hours shift, stationed at the water wells in the different sections of the camp, and they proceeded to chlorinate, using a standard chlorine solution, every bucket of water the women took from the well. When the cholera epidemic began to decline, we maintained these shifts only during the day.

As to the latrine building, we initiated a program whereby families who lacked a latrine were motivated to dig a hole of previously established dimensions, at least thirty feet (ten meters) from the living quarters and sixty feet (twenty meters) from any water source. After digging the hole, ARC supplied the necessary materials and personnel to construct the family latrine. The fact that each family dug its own pool served the purpose of creating incentive for maintenance and care of the latrine later. The community response was quite favorable. Furthermore, we installed a total of eight latrines of the VIP type (Ventilated Improved Pit latrines) around the Maternity and Health Center in Chang'ambika. Those who had to go into a regular latrine, out of either curiosity or necessity, could give testimony to the nauseating odors the interiors gave off. The foul smell attracted flies and cockroaches that, together with a lack of maintenance and cleaning, turned the latrine into a source of infection and into a place to be avoided. In the refugee camps, this situation occurred in the latrines meant for patient use. So those who, for the aforementioned reasons, preferred to perform their necessities out of doors contributed to the dissemination of illnesses and epidemics like cholera or dysentery. With the installation of the VIP latrines, the problem practically disappeared, since the system of double ventilating flues eliminated the odor, a grating averted the entrance of flies and other insects, the two-room structure offered privacy, and a minimum amount of light shunned the flies.

By March 1993, we were able to reduce the gross mortality rate by almost fifty percent as compared to the previous months, especially as compared to December's figures. Several factors contributed to this success, among them: (1) the beginning of the dry season, (2) a major effort on the part of the health team, and (3) logistic and administrative support. After delivering a situation report on the refugee camps in the Chikwawa district during the health meeting for the southern region, unaware that someone from the press was present, I was greatly surprised to read an article published in the national newspaper, the *Daily News*, dated March 30, 1993, where they reported these achievements. A few days later an emissary from the radio station MBC (Malawian Broadcasting Corporation), the only one in Malawi, interviewed me, asking that I give more details about the report. The interview was then broadcast throughout the entire country in the Chichewa language.

In truth, the political situation at the time was such that the official means of communication centered around the pursuit of "good news." The referendum that would decide whether the country would keep its present one-party regimen or would give way to a multiparty system was nearing, and surveys indicated that the government was behind in the polls. My report was one of the few "good news" notices that could be published for which part of the merit logically went to the Ministry of Health and its "adequate policy of coordination and collaboration with the NGOs (non-governmental organizations)." Once past the initial moment of surprise followed by a certain point of vanity for all the unexpected show of attention, I understood that I had been nothing more than a small pawn in an immense political game that was coming to a head in Malawi during this period. In fact, there were several factors involved—most of them out of my control—in the sharp decrease of the morbidity and mortality in most of the refugee camps. What did not fail to give me satisfaction was that in truth, the health situation in the camps was showing signs of convalescence, whether or not it was due to our direct intervention.

THE PANDEMIC OF THE CENTURY

April 1993

Noel Kondwani, clinical officer[1] for Kunyinda, had on many occasions demonstrated his excellent clinical and therapeutic skills, besides having an uncommonly selfless manner with his patients. I considered myself fortunate to have him as a part of the health team, in spite of the fact that he belonged to Malawi's Ministry of Health. On several occasions his wide knowledge about pathologies common to the zone proved vital in a diagnosis and opportune in the treatment of patients who might otherwise have died. During my first months in Africa, he became my tutor, due to my limited experience in diagnosing certain illnesses, especially skin diseases in black people. I never imagined how different skin rashes or skin infections manifest themselves in African people, turning an otherwise simple diagnosis into a complicated clinical procedure. For example, scabies—a common parasitic infection caused by the Sarcoptes scabies—produces red spots in the upper and lower extremities as well as on the abdomen of fair individuals. However, in black people the spots are of a dark brown color, which can lead to a misdiagnosis.

On many afternoons, Noel and I sat down together after work to enjoy the coolness of the setting sun and chatted about various subjects. There was no limit to his curiosity about that distant and mysterious country called Ecuador—a name that has always been associated with the line that represents 0° latitude. It never ceased to surprise him to learn about the number of similarities between Latin America and Africa. He was always prompt to alleviate whatever doubt or uneasiness I had about Malawi, a country that I was only beginning to understand.

After staying in Chang'ambika for a much longer time than usual, I returned to Kunyinda to learn that my young friend had been hospitalized with a diagnosis of reactivated tuberculosis, and that the physician assistant was covering his absence. For the first two weeks after his release from the hospital, Noel stayed on to rest in his hometown, returning to his duties after an absence of almost one month. The health personnel could not hide their joy in the clinical officer's return, and he immediately reinitiated his important work with his habitual good humor and serenity as if nothing had happened. However, within a few weeks I began to notice an evident loss of weight, which Noel continually denied. A short time later he returned to his bed, adducing what was bothering him to simply a slight malaise or a mild attack of malaria.

His absences from work were becoming more frequent and during one visit to his house I could see that his appearance was much altered, almost unrecognizable: he was extremely thin and cachectic, suffering with continual fevers and a persistent cough. As a friend it caused revulsion in me to accept the evidence that as a doctor was difficult to refute, but on seeing him I had to face the situation with Noel and put forth my concerns. My ques-

tions about high-risk sexual contacts received neg-
ative answers, as did questions about possible con-
tact with contaminated blood. It was clear that
Noel was not disposed to facing the cruel truth, and
I respected his decision.

The minister of health approved a request from
Noel that he be transported to a health unit near
his hometown, where some of his relatives lived.
My friend left, never to return. A few months later,
in January of 1994, I received notice of his death.
Noel had become one of the thousands of young
Africans who, in the fullness of life, succumbed to
the pandemic of this century: AIDS.

There have been reports of AIDS cases in Malawi since
the middle of the 1980s. A test to detect the HIV infection
was initiated in 1985. It determined that two percent of
the pregnant women who attended prenatal clinics were
HIV positive; that is to say that they had the AIDS virus
in their bodies. This number rose to twenty-three percent
in an urban prenatal center in 1990. By the end of 1993,
it was still forbidden to refer to AIDS as a national health
problem, and the government censured the scientific
investigations in the camp. The MCP government, led by
President Banda, wanted to present the image of a happy
nation that had eluded this epidemic, with the exception
of some "isolated cases." However, in 1994, the problem
had become so obvious that it was impossible to hide it
any longer. A study by Johns Hopkins University was the
first to cite the realistic facts as to the magnitude of the
epidemic: at that time, approximately one million
Malawians were infected with the HIV virus that caused
Acquired Immune Deficiency Syndrome, more commonly
known as AIDS. According to that study, ten percent of
the Malawi's population is HIV positive. A very high percentage (more than eighty percent) of the patients diagnosed with tuberculosis were HIV positive, and hospital
admissions for complications related to AIDS were clearly
rising. Also, according to these facts, Malawi has one of
the highest number of AIDS infected individuals in the
world.

The programs of many health organizations, including ARC's, have been reoriented toward the prevention of this grave problem. It will not be possible to evaluate the results of these actions for some time to come, but meanwhile such valuable individuals as my friend Noel continue to give up their lives to the implacable advancement of this terrible illness.

NOTES

1. The clinical officer carries out functions similar to those of a general physician, a professional rarity in Malawi.

7

OUTSIDE INFLUENCES

MALAWI'S HEALTH SYSTEM

It is appropriate at this point to quickly explain how the health system functions in this African country. A brief history of the introduction of Western medicine in southern Africa during the last century will help to explain why there is still a strong British influence in the health care field and others as well. As mentioned earlier, the first doctor to visit the region now known as Malawi was Dr. David Livingstone along with one of his traveling companions, Dr. John Kirk. The first physician to reside in the country was Dr. John Dickinson, a surgeon assigned to the Magomero Mission, who arrived in 1861. Others followed these pioneers, the majority of British origin: Dr. Robert Laws, who performed the first surgery (an arm amputation) in the country, and Dr. D.K. Cross. Many of them never returned to the land of their origin but succumbed to malaria or other local illnesses. Laws, the "old father," is still remembered in the country for his gentle manners and for his eagerness to serve the African people.

The first genuine hospital in Malawi was constructed in the mission at Blantyre in 1896 and would later become part of the new city hospital, named in 1958 the Queen Elizabeth Hospital, which is today one of the principal tertiary care centers in the country. Until only a few years ago, the only doctors in Malawi were of European origin. Even today, the country is very dependent upon foreign health professionals in order to fulfill the increasing demand for health care. Proof of this is that even during Banda's regime, the government awarded facilities to those physicians and nurses who had an interest in working in the country, although not so with journalists, who seldom received similar work visas. In 1993, the number of physicians in Malawi barely reached 262, the ratio being one doctor for each 36,023 inhabitants, although the World Health Organization (WHO) advises that the optimal ratio should be one doctor for every 600 to 700 inhabitants.

In the Malawi health system, health care personnel are categorized as follows: health surveillance assistants (HSA), health inspectors (HI), medical assistants (MA), clinical officers (CO), and general and specialist physicians (MD). The health surveillance assistants and the inspectors are responsible for carrying out community health programs, including immunization, health education, home visits. The medical assistants and clinical officers carry the heavy burden of providing heath care at the local and district level. Upon my arrival, I was annoyed to find that the medical assistant in Kunyinda seldom performed a complete physical examination of a patient; in most cases he never rose from his chair, and after listening to the complaint, he would just write a prescription on a piece of paper and call for the next patient. It did not take me long to realize that the number of patients that these health professionals saw each day was enormous. The few physicians in the country were in charge of the clinical and administrative procedures in the major hospitals (one in each of the three regions) and at the central and regional level.

The government authorities in the health field are the district health officers (DHO), regional health officers (RHO), and the minister of health. It is curious that many of the DHOs and RHOs are Dutch. Through an agreement for technical and financial cooperation between the two countries, it was established that doctors coming from the Netherlands would be in charge of the administrative and medical aspects of the hospitals at the district and regional levels.

Due to the limited number of physicians, it has turned out that the regular attention to clinics has fallen almost exclusively to the clinical officers and medical assistants who have adequate theoretical-practical preparation. Some of these have become such masters in their area of specialization that they are not much different from a general physician, especially in the practical aspects. In the last few years, outstanding students have received scholarships to study medicine in some European university, especially those in Britain. These new professionals were then obligated to serve the state for a minimum of four years before they were permitted to begin private practice. However, many of them saw it as an opportunity not to return to Malawi and, with degree in hand, began practices in Europe or in other African countries. In order to avoid this, the Malawi government reached an accord with the universities wherein the last hospital rotation before graduation as medical doctors was in Malawi. Ultimately, several foreign academics residing in Malawi met to form the first School of Medical Sciences of the University of Malawi. It is expected that the first generation of physicians to have their last year of study in their own country will be graduated in the near future. However, I question whether such an effort is cost-effective considering that the country cannot afford to locate most of the new graduates in the public health system. These physicians hired by the Ministry of Health, would still make less money than their colleagues working in the private sector, who mostly stay in urban areas. Perhaps, a regional medical school dealing specifically with the southeastern African region would be the most efficient approach, since it would meet the training needs of countries with historic, geographical, and cultural links such as Zambia, Zimbabwe and Malawi, which belonged in the past to the Rhodesian Federation. Shared costs and a larger faculty and student body would certainly benefit the region in an efficient way.

The responsibility for the health care at the rural level falls almost exclusively on the medical assistant, a professional who is prepared to manage those clinical cases most common in the country. As mentioned earlier, health inspectors and health surveillance assistants are in charge of primary and preventative care. Through this system, which mostly follows along the lines of the conference of Alma Ata as far as primary health care goes, the Malawian government tries to provide health care to broad rural sectors, although not even basic needs such as water and sanitation are available for the rural population. The health workers eventually will be left alone to deal with the major problems that the communities face every day, and they will loose motivation because of the lack of continuing education and on-the-job training, poor supervision, and the lack of feedback from the district administrators.

Every expatriate doctor who comes into the country to work for an international organization or for the government must undergo a practice period of at least three weeks in one of the three regional hospitals of the country. In my case, I fulfilled this requirement in Blantyre's Queen Elizabeth Hospital in three phases of one week each, and it was, to be sure, very beneficial. Mr. L. Chalila, a Malawian clinical officer who specialized in skin disorders, was a magnificent instructor, and in practicing with him I was able to observe lesions and illnesses that luckily are seen less frequently in Ecuador, i.e., secondary syphilis, Kaposi Sarcoma (in AIDS cases), pellagra, onchocercosis, *larva migrans*, tropical ulcers, etc. This rotation allowed me to further broaden my knowledge of the diagnosis and treatment of illnesses more common to the country and would prove to be very valuable to me in the following months in Africa.

At the time of my arrival, Malawi was "invaded" by numerous organizations that were providing technical cooperation, especially aimed at the refugee population. Multilateral organizations (UNHCR, UNICEF, UNFPA), bilateral agencies (USAID, GTZ) and non-governmental organizations (MSF, ARC, Jesuit Refugee Service, International Rescue Committee, Save the Children UK, World Vision, International Eye Foundation) were providing logistic and technical support to the country. In fact, they were providing much needed assistance, in some cases the only one available. An international health scholar might disagree with me for calling it "assistance," but to me technical cooperation involves a similar effort from the national counterpart, something that Malawi was in no position to offer. In a later chapter I will describe this important issue in more detail.

TUTORING AGREEMENTS WITH FOREIGN UNIVERSITIES

At the beginning of 1993, the American Refugee Committee signed an agreement with the (U.S.) Columbia University School of Medicine in New York through which a small group of two or three medical students, at the end of their studies, could do a community health practice with the different ARC programs in Malawi. The most important component of this field practice was a rotation through the refugee camps, these rotations being under my direction, for which I had to prepare work itineraries for the young graduate students. The itineraries were composed of rounds in the Intensive Nutrition Center and in the cholera units and, among others, supervised training of the local personnel.

The first North American students arrived in April from Columbia University: Anne Davis and Mary Beth Gayle. The practice had been organized in such a manner that only one doctor at a time would be in the camp. Both young ladies arrived during a period when the daily admissions were numerous and all our services and work were stretched to the limit. Mary Beth, the first to arrive at Chang'ambika, was a tall, red-headed young woman whose compassionate character toward those in need became evident to the refugees and medical personnel. During the first few days I found time to explain our function and the care of our patients in the different services: the Intensive Nutrition Center, the Nutrition Clinic, and the Cholera, Dysentery and Respiratory Care Units. It was evident that Mary Beth had a good general theoretical knowledge but limited practice with patients, and at first she had difficulty in accepting the fact that she would have to do case histories, give physical examinations, make diagnoses, and perform treatments for the patients she was assigned—all with relatively little supervision. Little by little she gained confidence, although with the more difficult cases she always consulted me before beginning the appropriate treatment.

Anne Davis arrived a little later and began her work following the same plan as her colleague, who had by then successfully completed her rotation. Mary Beth's sweetness was replaced with a contagious energy that Anne was always able to muster. A blond New Yorker, open minded and quite tolerant of racial, religious, and gender differences, Anne was a unique companion during the two weeks she spent in the Chang'ambika refugee camp. She was a person who displayed noncompliance toward any type of injustice, and she had no qualms about expressing her views to the office personnel at the ARC headquarters in Blantyre for the "excessive comfort and luxury in which they lived while the field personnel, who were doing the true work, lacked even the basic necessities." This criticism earned her a letter of censure from the ARC Director, John Keys, sent to the director of international programs at Columbia University.

The most interesting part of this experience was that both observed and actively participated in the community health program for refugees, which included prenatal care, growth and development programs, immunization, nutritional follow-up, and the training of community health workers and health education. As part of their assignments, they gave a weekly talk to the health personnel in each camp on a relevant health theme that they had previously discussed with them and later with me. This experience was also valuable to me, because being a tutor brings a new focus to the work in the camp, and the frequent questions and commentaries added a new perspective to the daily routine. Likewise, their curiosity forced a continual preparedness in me, and each night we discussed the problems that had faced us during the day, and we made plans for the following day.

This is the type of experience that Ecuadorian medical students lack. Our training focuses exclusively on medicine, and our training remains enclosed within the walls of the hospital. As soon as we graduate and with little orientation we must serve the year of rural medicine in a local health center, where we realize that there are no "interesting cases" or, in other words, unusual pathologies that attract our attention and call upon our diagnostic skills. In the village, people suffer and die of common diseases: acute diarrheal and respiratory infections, immune-preventable diseases. As rural doctors, we must face problems that go beyond our clinical expertise, and we are not prepared to assume a leadership role in the community because we do not know how to lead a group discussion, or how to administer the health center and its human and material resources. During training, our mentors never discuss water and sanitation issues, and our epidemiology course is a review of infectious agents, always from the clinical perspective. How I longed for this type of field practice and tutoring for Ecuadorian students, where they could learn from actual experience and apply concepts of health promotion, primary health care, and preventative medicine in the community. What a pleasure it would have been to dedicate all this time toward helping train my fellow countrymen and countrywomen in an area of medicine that our country needs so badly.

Subsequently, a group of five doctors from Zambia, Uganda, and one from Guatemala were to arrive; a group obtaining their masters degrees in tropical medicine at the University of Liverpool, England, who were to make one field rotation in Malawi. Under my supervision, they did their practice in the Intensive Nutrition Center during a one-week stay in the camp at Chang'ambika. The fact that there was one Latin American among them was reason for much satisfaction on the part of this Ecuadorian, who did not miss the opportunity to speak Spanish, after so many months of not being able to use the language of Cervantes.

LAKE OF STARS

At last, after almost four months in the country, I was able to visit Lake Malawi. It had often been said that Malawi was the "land of the lake," since this lake covered an area of 8,878 square miles (23,000 square kilometers), that is to say, one-fifth of the total area of the country, and it being the third largest lake in Africa. After forging upstream in 1859, Livingstone discovered what would become known as Lake Nyasa, which would give the country its name, Nyasaland, until its independence from Great Britain, when the lake and the nation would come to be named Malawi.

Taking advantage of the Easter Week vacation, John Newohner and I set out on a trip to the north, passing by Liwonde and Mangochi for the tiny town of Cape McClear on the south shore of this immense lake. What strikes one at first is the cleanliness of its blue and crystal water in which one can easily see the great variety of fish of many colors, which has given Lake Malawi its well-deserved fame for being the most important emporium of exotic fresh water fish in the world. Cape McClear was the location of the seat of one of the first Christian missions in the country, founded at the end of the past century, and from where expeditions left heading for the most distant points on the map with the object of continuing their evangelical labors, establishing health posts, or directing military operations against rebellious tribes or against those who were in the slave trade. Cape McClear is a little town that survives on fishing and, more lately, on tourism. The time-honored huts of clay and straw were being replaced with more sophisticated but small one-story buildings of adobe and cement, which fill the function of lodgings known as "rest houses" or of restaurants. Images alluding to the type of business within were painted in brilliant colors on the facades—a person of color in bed, a family enjoying a big plate of *n'zima*, fish of every kind.

It seemed strange to me to see in such an idyllic place the rather large number of tourists known as "backpackers," most of them from European countries, but some from North America and Australia. Tourists from within Malawi were scarce, and the only Africans there were local residents or the few business proprietors. The area was surrounded by hills covered with vegetation of acacia, mango, cottonwood trees, and unending thickets of medium height. There are paths that go over and around this mountainous area from which one can still see some of the flora and fauna native to this sector. Until the 1950's, it was still common to encounter leopards, antelopes, and a large variety of monkeys. Today, the only wild animals easily found are the mandrills and monkeys that maraud the campgrounds hoping to steal food from the tourists. The quantity and variety of fish is impressive in this area, which is a part of the water reserve belonging to the Lake Malawi National Park. Besides the fish, the lake houses a large number of hippopotamus and crocodiles that take refuge in the more separated and uninhabited regions of the lake although, on occasion, a hippopotamus can be seen near the beaches of Cape McClear.

The climate is hot, 100 to 105 degrees Fahrenheit (38 to 40 degrees Celsius) on the average, but this was not a novelty since we had come from temperatures exceeding this, from a place where there was no lake to refresh ourselves from the heat. The sunsets were poetic, and by the evenings when the sun was beginning its rapid descent, everyone suspended whatever he or she were doing to admire the symphony of colors that accompanied the occasion. A magic moment took hold of each person who was there to witness that fleeting instant; pictures were drawn on the cirrus and cumulus clouds in the sky, which took on impossible colorations ranging from faint orange tones to an intense red. At the same time, little by little, the constellations began to appear, twinkling their light years of antiquity. The darkness fell like a mantel that suddenly appeared over our shoulders. As the shadows began to dominate, we were still left with such ecstasies from nature's symphony that even the imminence of the night could not awaken us from such a profound dream of the absent vision.

Before leaving the "lake of the stars," I had a feeling that this would not be my last time visit there. Because of its close proximity, I had recuperated from months of work and sacrifice. It was inevitable that in a few more weeks I would again need this marvelous therapy.

A few months later, I would indirectly participate in a project intended to establish the causes for the rise in

69

the incidence of schistosomiasis, an illness caused by the parasite *Schistosoma hæmatobium, mansoni* or *japonicum*, the two species being the more common in Africa. The intermediate host for this parasite is a snail of the genus *Bulinus* or the genus *Physopsis* that lives in water, and in Lake Malawi it is a part of the diet for some fresh water fish. This illness produces urinary and gastrointestinal complications, depending on the species. The hypothesis was that excessive fishing in certain areas of the lake had permitted an increase in the snail population, which, in turn, had augmented the number of infectious parasites. A team of investigators took a count of a certain variety of fish in order to compare these figures with the corresponding figures taken ten years earlier in the same area. In what would be my first session at scuba diving, I collaborated in the counting activity, although I was more worried about how to keep myself from floating, for I forgot to take with me the weights that I was supposed to wear around my waist. The results of the study confirmed a dangerous decrease in the fish population in the area near Cape McClear.

NUTRITION IN MALAWI

The food in Malawi is very simple, and the people sustain themselves most of all with corn. How interesting that a foodstuff originally from my part of the world has become the main diet of people in Malawi and other African nations. Family crops base their production on this product from which, through a complicated process of drying, grinding and refining, they produce a white corn flour known as *ufa*. Many times there have been attempts to introduce into the camps a whole grain corn flour called *ngaiwa* considered more nutritive, but it was badly received by the refugees, who prefer the refined flour. Again, the Western influence for more refined products became evident, resulting in a less nutritious diet and, perhaps more importantly, in a change of attitudes toward certain foods.

    N'zima is the principal dish of the Malawian diet, prepared basically from white corn flour mixed with water to obtain a pasty consistency. The flavor is rather flat, so it's accompanied by beans, pumpkin leaves with peanut sauce, and dried fish or goat meat. Before beginning to eat, the lady of the house brings a receptacle of water and, one by one, the diners wash their hands as the woman, in a very reverent manner and without making the eye contact, offers the water to each one. An order is well established, in that the masculine guest is the first to wash his hands followed by the father of the host family. The women—with the exception of girls who still have not had their first menstrual period—do not eat with the rest of the family and must content themselves with whatever is left over. Having finished with the washing and using his right hand, the Malawian begins to shape the n'zima dough which he is served in order to put the other foods on it. N'zima is present at every meal of the day in every region of the country, including the area of Lake Malawi.

One of the most appetizing dishes in Malawi is *chambo*, a variety of fish that comes from the lake and one that I had the opportunity to enjoy on more than one occasion. The flavor is reminiscent of sea bass, although it has a much lighter consistency. This nutritious food is available to the Malawian who lives in the neighborhood of the lake or in the city. The lack of refrigeration makes it impossible to enjoy chambo in the interior rural sectors, where the only available fish is dried. The abundance of edible fish in the lake means that the population living near the shores has fewer malnutrition problems, which is not so for those in the interior of the country, where, in 1985, malnutrition in children under five years of age was the cause of 11.2 percent of hospital deaths and where anæmia produced 9.1 percent of the deaths in the same age group.

According to the season one can enjoy a limited variety of local fruits. Papayas and pineapple are difficult to get, but not so mango, a fruit introduced from Asia, which in season can be found throughout the country. Yucca, or cassava, introduced from South America nearly 300 years ago, and is eaten raw or cooked, together with the never-to-be-missed n'zima.

71

It is surprising to watch groups of people who, during the off-season, put themselves to the task of collecting flying termites, which are then fried and seasoned with salt and *piri piri*, and thus consumed. I had the opportunity to "enjoy" this African dish during one of my walks through the local market, and I must admit that, after initial rejection, it tasted not so different from a certain kind of chip. The feared piri piri is a variety of hot dried pepper, ground and converted into a red powder, that is added to almost every food.

8

THE ROAD CONTINUES

Mid-year Experiences

May 24, 1993

*Already six months have passed by since my arrival
in Africa, and many occurrences have taken place
in that short time. The balance sheet at the end of
the first semester is positive, and I have high expec-
tations for the months to come. May was a month
of planning for what will be the second half of my
contract. I really cannot state that I have a routine
for work, since the conditions at the middle of the
year don't allow one to predict much ahead of time
what the future would present in a refugee camp.
I am continually traveling and I seldom sleep in
the same bed for more than four or five nights in a
row. It is a rare week when I do not have to make
one or more trips to Blantyre, Mwanza, Chikwawa,
or Kunyinda.*

*I continue on alone in Chang'ambika since ARC
still has not been able to sign a contract with a
nurse in the United States. However, this absence
of an expatriate professional has been satisfacto-
rily covered by local personnel, even though I find
myself obliged to spend more time in Chang'ambika*

and to limit my supervisory visits in Kunyinda to a maximum of one-and-a-half weeks per month. On the other hand, Africa continually fascinates me, and I believe that gradually the mystery and charm of this continent is penetrating my veins and settling deep within me. As I am writing these words, the children of N'Gona, as on many other nights, are busy at their children's games that I remember from my own childhood: rounds, pájaras pintas and florones.[1] It's a shame that in the Western world, including my Ecuador, these traditional children's games are being lost little by little, replaced by video games, television, and Nintendo.

As for other sounds, the Malawi night is full of them, but lately I've had trouble falling asleep because of the night's visitors. Cockroaches can be very noisy at times, and there have been nights when they've awakened me from a deep sleep as they set themselves to eating the boxes where I keep my various belongings. I also discovered a nest of rats behind the dresser where I keep my clothes, sadly, after the rodents had already finished off several articles of my underwear and shirts so that they were unwearable. After a while Pedro, the cook, and one of the guards caught two of the rodents. The curious thing about the case is that after capturing them, the cook proceeded with what appeared to be a divvying up of them, and instead of throwing them into the trash, carefully wrapped them in pieces of newspaper and placed them in a corner of the kitchen. At the end of their day's work, Peter and Mateya took the little packages out of the house while I continued to think the final destiny of the rats was in the trash. The next morning upon asking about the luck of the rats, Peter answered me that his wife had fixed them for dinner that night...! My appetite was not so good for the rest of the day, and even so now when I remember that it was my own cook who considers rat to be a delicacy.

One night in the N'Gona house, I was sleeping peacefully under the mosquito netting when there was a noise from something that had crashed against the bed, and I awoke with a start. In the total darkness it was impossible for me to identify the cause of such a strange noise, and I cannot deny that I was filled with panic. After a few seconds there was a squeak like that of a rat's and a subsequent bump against the netting confirmed that my imagination was not playing games on me. The thought of leaving the bed to get a candle in order to identify the reason for this noise gave me chills, but I knew it was the only alternative I had if I wanted to get some rest that night. Arming myself with courage, at one of the pauses I got out of bed and felt my way around to find the candle first and then the box of matches atop the night table. With trembling hands I was finally able to light the candle, put it on the table, and took refuge back in bed. Then, a black shadow came down from a corner of the ceiling and flew toward the new source of light. After a moment of fright, I was able to identify the sinister figure: It was a bat.

It is strange how darkness can convert such a harmless animal into a sinister creature. The noise was not going to let me sleep, so I moved to the room next door for the rest of the night. The next day, I realized that two bats had nested in a hole at the corner of the ceiling in my room and during the night, they turned into acrobatic pilots, waking up the human who happened to sleep in their playground. Pedro was able to capture one, but I could not allow its execution and we let it free. The bat was back that night. We did not realize that its radar-like system would guide it back to the nest. After several days of peaceful room-sharing, night flying became less frequent and human and animal occupants learned to accept each other's presence. However, when the opportunity came to repair the roof outside my room, I made sure to include a plug for the hole, and my roommates were forced to find a new place for mating and a new playground other than my room.

In spite of all this unforeseen fauna, every day the house at N'Gona looked more and more hospitable. I had been buying some trinkets and decorations as well as some ornamental plants that were changing the face of the place little by little. Truly, this was turning into a home. On the other hand, they had installed solar panels a few days before, and from then on the nights were less dark, and I was able to work indefinitely at the computer without fear that the battery would die, or that I would have to wait until the next trip to Blantyre to recharge it. Later, ARC workers under the supervision of Stanley Banda built a hygienic service and a shower, so that the hateful trips to the antique latrine became a part of history.

NOTES
1. Traditional Ecuadorian children's games.

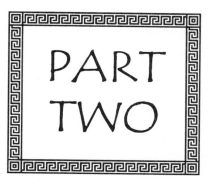

PART
TWO

9

THE UNKNOWN CONTINENT

June 1993

*I thought I had become accustomed to the contin-
uous beat of the drums that sometimes lasted for
hours. At times it was the only sound that broke
the tranquillity of N'Gona, a remote village in
Malawi very close to the Mozambican frontier, a
village whose population belonged almost in its
entirety to the ethnic group called Chewa. That
Friday, however, the sound of that intoxicating
rhythm had continued from the afternoon and
throughout the night, except for short intervals
when the musicians possibly rotated or took a well-
deserved rest. On Saturday, the drums and songs
continued throughout the day, so I judged that this
time we were dealing with a different kind of celebration, perhaps of more importance than those
traditional ones where the music commemorated
weddings, births, and deaths. My curiosity was
piqued when the hypnotizing, almost magical beat,
continued during the second night. It was evident,
given the large number of voices singing and the
general volume that a large part of the community*

had come together. Surprisingly, I was able to drop off to sleep, but on Sunday morning I could resist my curiosity no longer, and, accompanied by one of the young boys with whom I usually played soccer on weekends, I made my way to the place where the commotion originated.

Crossing the bridge over the Gaga River we came to some dwellings that were extensions of the small village. Outside one of these huts, dozens of men and women seemed to be gathering. Everyone showed signs of physical weariness, but at the same time their faces indicated they were in a state of trance, intoxicated by the rhythm and something else that I could not determine. Although these people were my own neighbors, they were now almost unrecognizable; their manner was much more aggressive and the women allowed themselves to look me directly in the eyes, something that would never have happened under normal circumstances. The men had lost their timidity as well as their assumed attitude of servility in front of a white man, and they spoke to me directly, although of course, in the local Chichewa dialect. Perhaps the only ones who remained untouched by the collective fever were the children, who ran around the surroundings, playing as they had always. Seeing the state of the adults, my initial impulse was to leave the place immediately, despite the fact that until this moment I had always felt safe in the company of these humble people. The children's attitude made me change my mind, since I could detect from their expressions that most of them had already seen, although not participated in a similar ceremony, and that I, therefore, had nothing to fear. After several minutes, people no longer took of notice of my presence, and I was better able to appreciate what was happening.

A middle-aged woman seemed to be the central focus of the ceremony. Her insensible face showed clear signs of exhaustion, but her eyes held a strange vigor that made her state of exaltation even *more evident. When the beating of the drums seemed to subside, going into one of the few but far in between pauses, the woman suddenly began to dance frenetically, simultaneously singing or chanting in Chichewa. A second, older woman circled around her one way and then another, matching the earlier participants of the ceremony, and from time to time she launched imprecations that seemed like orders directed toward the gathering or toward the dancer. When the strength of the dancer began to falter, other women approached her with a receptacle of liquid that I assumed was water. Much later I saw that it was taken from over-sized vessels that did not contain water but a liquid that in some ways reminded me of our own traditional "chicha."[1] After a brief pause, the dance continued with even more energy to the point that the woman could hold up no longer and collapsed to the floor. The other participants immediately carried her away. The musicians took advantage of this moment to take one of their short breaks, and I took advantage of the pause to leave. It didn't surprise me that after a few minutes the drums began once again. The woman was probably back again, recuperated, reinitiating her exotic dance that continued on for the third consecutive night.*

In the days that followed, I didn't let myself think too much about that massive transformation, since by Monday it already seemed to have been forgotten. The people turned to their daily labors and resumed their usual attitudes. After several attempts, which were courteously rebuffed, I finally found someone who was willing to give me an explanation of what had happened over the weekend. Lamentably, Pedro did not speak English well, but that did not keep him from explaining until I could understand that I had been witness to a rare celebration in which a member of the community (the woman) who is possessed by "spirits" is "cured." Pedro maintained that it was not the woman who was singing and dancing but the spirit that possessed her who repulsed the husband for

81

having another woman and for not providing for the home, wife, and children as he had before. This explanation came to mind again on my next visit to Zomba, and I mentioned it to my friend Mitchel Strumpf, a North American musicologist from Chancellor University. He furnished me with a document on several studies about the music and dance in Malawi (A.B. Chilivumbo, *Vimbuza or Mashawe: A Mystic Therapy*).

According to the document, there are traditional dances and music with therapeutic purposes like the Vimbuza songs and Mashawe dances in the northern and central part of Malawi. The woman in the dance, as I learned later, having withdrawn gradually from the community, had fallen into a rigorous silence that was interrupted only periodically by conversations with herself and by abnormal gestures. Later, her situation worsened, and she also began to neglect her duties as mother and housewife. If we take into account that rural Africans are rather social individuals that derive a great part of their moral and psychosocial support from other members of the community, then a distancing from the communal system implies grave consequences for the person and the family. A community such as this must create mechanisms that allow the individual to be reincorporated into its social nucleus before the situation becomes even worse. In the African village, there are a series of traditional mechanisms that, from time immemorial, have been utilized towards therapeutic ends, and that have subsequently restrengthened the community's identity.

It is appropriate to mention that for a woman in Malawi's rural society, as well as in the continent at large, there are a series of social restrictions. From early childhood they learn to play a different role from boys, which becomes evident in the types of games they play and responsibilities they acquire. Females are responsible for taking care of their younger siblings; they collect water; they help their mothers in the kitchen. The strict division of labor with men is more obvious later in life, and females submit to the male will—father, brother, or husband—most of their lives. Women are not supposed to demonstrate anger or to raise their voice in public, and they cannot look directly into man's eyes. In the case of the woman at N'Gona, her husband had taken another woman long before and was no longer caring for the home. It seems that feelings of anger, frustration, and impotency were slowly building up in the woman to the point that the first symptoms and signs of social maladjustment were beginning to show. Therefore, the community found itself obliged to make use of one of their resources—the therapeutic dance.

As A. B. Chilivumbo explained in his study of mystical therapy through dance, the community knowingly gives space to the woman who, through dance and song, can freely express her emotions, feelings, and frustrations, all of which constitute an important escape valve. Attributing the symptomatology to a "possession by spirits" makes it easier to justify and pardon the rupture of the social code, referring to her submission. At the same time, the wayward husband, in this case the cause of the emotional imbalance, is pressured, indeed forced by the community, to change his ways. The result is the return to normality and the reinsertion of the individual back into the communal nucleus. Sadly, this rural way of life is disappearing as the urban centers continue their disorderly growth, unable to cope with the social and cultural needs of those who have been forced to leave the countryside in search of better opportunities in life. The result is a loss of identity and those values that only the tribal community can offer.

After this experience, the very sight of the "woman of N'Gona" never failed to surprise me. Whether she was grinding corn, or carrying water from the river or talking and laughing with her neighbors—in other words—carrying on a normal life, each time I saw her, it became more and more difficult for me to relate her to that same woman consumed by frenetic dancing, singing in a loud voice messages that I only now understand were reproaches against her husband's attitude, drinking a concoction that not only rehydrated and nourished her but at the same time drew her into a frenzy of falls and leaps for hours that finally turned into days. And I never stopped silently thanking her for having involuntarily permitted me to witness a part of this ceremony that, though uncommon, does represent the true Africa, the disappearing Africa.

THE LATIN AMERICAN COMMUNITY

It was not until the month of May 1993 that I had my first contact with another Latin American. I learned through Patricia Capwell, the ARC doctor in Mwanza, that only a few days before an Argentine doctor had arrived to take on the job of medical coordinator for Médecins Sans Frontières in the refugee camps in the Mwanza District. On one of my visits to Blantyre, I saw an MSF auto approaching us from the opposite direction, and beside the chauffeur in the car there was also a person with a massive beard who, it seemed, was also trying to catch a look at me. Both vehicles stopped almost simultaneously. We both got out, and as we went toward each other, all doubts vanished; we shook hands, and the Latin American Spanish began to flow as we made our respective introductions. For me it had been five long months, except for brief moments, since I had had the pleasure of speaking in my own lovely language.

Guillermo Bertoletti is a pediatric physician from Rosario, Argentina, of Italian descent, and was the new Latin American arrival in these distant lands. He had a long list of experiences behind him: Sri Lanka and Angola had been his other missions with MSF and now Malawi. Having a leftist tendency, Guillermo had taken an active part in the fight against human rights violations in his country during the "Dirty War." Later, he left Argentina to sail the seven seas, finally involving himself with Médecins Sans Frontières.

On the day of our chance encounter, Guillermo invited me to an Argentine *asado*,[2] which several members of the tiny South American community in Malawi also attended. It was a surprise for me to learn that there was a small but dynamic group of Latin American compatriots, and I longed to meet them. It was thus that one Sunday in May, I attended a typical asado, complete with wine, guitar, and the always warm company of our people. Also in attendance were Roberto Meier, an Argentine, who at that time was the director of the financial area of the United Nations High Commissioner for Refugees in Malawi; his wife, Graciela; Mirta and Jerry Steffen, an Argentine and North American, respectively, with whom I developed a deep friendship; and María Inés Johnston Molina, an Argentine doctor who had initially come to Malawi with her Irish husband for one year but already had been there for twenty.

With the objective of getting the exact number of Latin Americans residing or working in Malawi, I wrote to the Department of Immigration for a listing, by country, which was delivered to me a few weeks later. As of June 30, 1993, citizens from the following South American countries were registered: Colombia, 1; Perú, 2; Bolivia, 1; Chile, 4; Argentina, 3; and Ecuador, 1 (me). Later, the number grew with the arrival of a young lady from Guayaquil (Ecuador), Esther Cornejo, who arrived with an Italian engineer under contract by Cogefarimpresit, the company that was building a dam on the Shire River. In the months that followed, I would have the opportunity to know and to appreciate my lone compatriot who would live in Malawi for eight months.

NOTES

1. *Chicha* is a strong drink made from fermented corn by the native Indian population in the high Andes.
2. *Asado* is a typical roast or barbecue found in Argentina and in other Latin American countries.

10

A TALE OF TWO DISTRICTS AND TWO CONTINENTS

··

CHANG'AMBIKA'S HEALTH FAIR

From the beginning of May through June 11, my life was turned into a whirl of events that kept me and dozens of workers in the two camps extremely busy. The First Health Poster Contest on May 22 was an event intended to attract the attention and participation of the students from the local school in Chang'ambika in regard to matters of community interest, in this case, health related. The response was excellent, and fifty-three students from the Chewa and Yao ethnic groups, from eight to thirty-one years old, enrolled and participated in the event, which consisted of designing a poster on the theme of health for the community. Because of my friendship with José Ignacio García, a Spanish Jesuit my age who was at that time working to reorganize the destroyed education system in the border region of Mozambique, which included the refugee camps, we were able to obtain the active participation of the Jesuit Refugee Service (JRS) in organizing and financing the contest. The UNHCR leant its support by giving economic prizes to the ten winners, whose works were then exhibited during the health fair, which I will discuss later. During two previous meetings, we had highlighted the themes of major interest on community health to the contestants, leaving the participants free to choose their subject for illustration. At the second meeting we had also given them materials to make their initial designs, which the health personnel under my supervision would then review and correct, in order to avoid incoherent messages and confusion. Everyone had access to brochures, in the Chichewa dialect that served as guides and gave clear and short messages about community health.

On the day of the contest, the JRS donated paper, a set of colored pencils, and an eraser, materials that each participant could keep after the contest. For two hours, the students, divided into age categories, put all their efforts toward presenting their best work possible. Earlier, a committee consisting of representatives from JRS, ARC, the school, the Ministry of Health for Malawi, and the medical director for UNHCR had been named, and they were to select the best works. Using previously established qualifying criteria, the committee rated each poster, and the ten best received prizes in a special ceremony. The most popular prizes were the money prizes that the UNHCR had donated and the traditional Ecuadorian figures of *masapán* that I had brought with me from Calderón.[1]

Organizing the Health Poster Contest, however, was child's play compared with the magnitude of organizing the First Refugee Health Fair, which was held in Chang'ambika's refugee camp. At the camp we fell into the habit of joking that everything from then on would be dated "before" or "after" the health fair—an activity that escalated to such a point that the preplanning in no way resembled the event that took place on June 11. The idea was born in Kunyinda during a soccer game between the camp team and a team from a neighboring village. The match attracted hundreds of refugees, who followed each nuance of the encounter with great intensity. It was evident that this type of distraction was very rare for them, and that community participation at any such event would be multitudinous. Therefore, if we could successfully induce a large congregation to attend and take advantage of the opportunity to offer talks on health care, to present some dramas on health themes, to vaccinate children, to provide prenatal checkups for mothers who otherwise would not come to the health center, the benefits would be incalculable.

The idea began to mature and included such diverse activities as condom distribution with demonstrations of condom use, handcraft workshops for women, traditional dances, and live music. The working sessions I had with my staff, trying to resolve the innumerable problems that presented themselves during the organization of the fair were countless. Imagine feeding approximately 450 people in two hours, coordinating the talks on health education that would be given simultaneously, organizing food and housing for the dozens of integrants in the theater, sports, and dance groups who would come from other parts of the country, and also organizing the distribution of 20,000 condoms to those who attended the respective demonstrations! We decided not to hand out condoms to those who did not attend the demonstration/talk, having as an antecedent the experience of a young refugee who was found chewing a condom as if it were chewing gum!

Shortly before the designated day of the health fair, we confirmed the participation of drama, dance, and music groups from Liwonde, Mwanza, Zomba, Blantyre, Kunyinda, Chikwawa, and N'Gabu. The simplistic idea of a local event had slowly been transformed into a regional happening that had repercussions much grander than we had initially intended. On a map we circumscribed the areas destined to be the fairgrounds, to be comprised of the soccer field and its surroundings, all situated in Section 11 of the Chang'ambika camp. We constructed a series of buildings in the traditional style, which would house the rooms for the educational talks and the handcraft workshops, and one *cabaña* for logistical support, which would serve as my general headquarters. Furthermore, we added ten newly constructed latrines around the soccer field and six tanks of chlorinated water for human consumption; the latter placed in strategic locations. The health team was prepared for whatever contingency might come and the then-near-empty Respiratory Care Unit was converted into a center for emergency care. The International Red Cross placed at our disposition four tents and personnel to take care of minor cases on location.

With only a week before the great event, I had the misfortune of falling ill with my second malaria attack of the year. Luckily, this one was much less severe than the first, and, in any case, it gave me a badly needed rest. After two days of convalescence at María Inés Molina's house in Blantyre, I was completely recuperated and ready to continue on with the last preparations. It was during these few days that the idea of writing a book began to germinate, as I was enjoying reading some of the works on African themes from an impressive library belonging to Frank Johnston, María Inés' husband. The first notes and compilations began in bed, as I fought off a tenacious fever.

Early in the morning of June 11, I went to supervise the last details of the event. Delegations from several cities and refugee camps had begun to arrive on the previous afternoon, and I was trying to reassure myself that everything would be ready by 9:00 a.m., the opening hour of the fair. One of my fears concerned the dreaded "African hour," which is no later than the infamous "Ecuadorian hour," but indeed a major retardant; for an event planned with such activities, a considerable delay in one of them could complicate the whole itinerary.

We had prepared identification for all the participants, that is for those who would have access to the assigned areas of housing and food distribution. We had sent invitations to all the international organizations that worked with refugees as well as to the authorities of the government's Ministry of Health. We also sent invitations to the media. The program consisted of the following activities:

- Immunization and Under-Five Clinics.
- Participation of the Local School: "Macuaela Dance" and drama about early parenthood.
- Health Talks: AIDS prevention and condom use, hygiene and sanitation, community participation.

- Traditional Music and Dances: "Chiwele" dancers, "The Zomba Melody Makers" from Chancellor College, N'Yao dancers, Valimba dance.
- Drama Groups: "Kankao." Kunyinda drama group: "AIDS, we could be at risk."
- Sports: Soccer match between Kunyinda vs. Chang'ambika.
- Exhibitions: Health posters and community handcrafts.

The ARC personnel had worked tirelessly for several weeks and had tried to foresee any eventuality. On the other hand, my functions were not limited to supervising the event but also included receiving the official delegations, resolving last minute problems, giving interviews to the media, and being in constant motion. During one of the musical presentations, as a surprise to the participants, I accepted an invitation from Ricardo García, the French/Spanish guitarist, to perform various numbers, one of them, "Bamboleo" by the Gypsy Kings, which really caused a sensation. By 3:00 p.m., the special guests began to leave the camp, and only the African people stayed to watch the king of sports, the soccer game. The day ended with the triumph of Chang'ambika, 3 to 1, and with the organizer of the event wearing the local colors. I was not sure that I would be able to play until shortly before the game, when the majority of the delegations left the camp. I decided to play midfield for Chang'ambika's team, although a little before the end of the first period I had to leave the field with a leg cramp, something that proved entertaining to the majority of those present, because it was the only time the ARC first aid team was called into action.

Without a doubt, the First Refugee Health Fair had been the biggest event of its kind in the region. Of the more than 5,000 people assembled, there were 150 ARC personnel; 300 musicians, dancers, health educators, immunization personnel, Ministry of Health employees, and school teachers; 100 guests from government and nongovernmental organizations; and approximately 4,000 refugees who directly participated in and enjoyed the event. Community participation was outstanding, and local leaders, chiefs, and healthcare workers participated actively throughout the day. People from the surrounding areas came to take part in the activities, and we were able to vaccinate the children and to make a nutritional assessment for those under five who seldom came to the health center. I could include statistics of the number of children immunized or the number of condoms distributed, but they would not reflect the degree of involvement or the joy the refugees experienced during that day. Quantity evaluation is the most common method used to assess a given program or activity, but in many cases it is not enough to present an accurate picture of the situation. In my report of the health fair, I included data such as the number of participants, immunizations, under-five clinics, condoms, but they hardly assess the depth of the community's motivation during and after the event or the emotional and physical involvement of people used to spending their days without recreation, days without activities that promote health. Some might wonder what a soccer game and a handcraft workshop have to do with health. Recreation, security, violence prevention, supportive environments are all components of a more comprehensive concept of health in which promotion and prevention are key ingredients.

I should mention that UNHCR's director general in Malawi attended as did their finance director and field officer. Other representatives came from organizations such as the International Red Cross, Médecins Sans Frontières, UNICEF, Save the Children, and JRS. The regional director of health and some district directors of health were also present. The Malawi Broadcasting Corporation, the single radio network in the country, as well as the *Daily News*, the newspaper with the highest circulation, sent several of their reporters to cover the fair. Later, in an article entitled "No Problem with Guillermo and Benjamin," *Reflections* magazine, which has broad distribution throughout the country, referred to the fact that for the first time two Latin American doctors, Guillermo Bertoletti (from Argentina) and myself (from

Ecuador), had joined forces in the two neighboring Malawi districts, Mwanza and Chikwawa, to improve health conditions for thousands of Mozambican refugees. According to the article, "The doctors, who come from South America, work in an area where life once seemed hardly worth a pinch of the salt, which, like all the other basics of life, remains in such short supply among these homes for the homeless." It went on to mention that in organizing Chang'ambika's First Health Fair we had discovered a successful formula, combining demonstrations on proper healthcare with community and sports activities. In a photograph on the front page, a smiling refugee child from the Chang'ambika camp posed, wearing a shirt printed with the words "No Problem," which served as the inspiration for the article's title.

NEW ARC PERSONNEL

At last, in June of 1993, a new nurse arrived in Chang'ambika. Lou Cooney, a North American, is a physician assistant (PA), meaning that she has the ability to examine, diagnose, and prescribe medicine. From then on I was freed from certain routine functions for which Lou was well trained, and I could direct my efforts to other areas of community health. A native of Boston, Lou learned to enjoy the simple things of life and never learned to drive a car, for as she said, it was an "unnecessary luxury in a city with good public transportation."

A few weeks after Lou's arrival, a malnourished child died on her arms after several long days of constant struggle against death—a confrontation that drained us physically and emotionally. It was a sad moment indeed, especially after we had generated some hope for a better outcome. Embracing each other, the child's mother and Lou cried for a long, long time. During the next few days, Lou showed signs of grief that affected her work at the Intensive Nutrition Center. I thought it was important to discuss the issue, and I told her that I was feeling sorry for the child too, but there were other children who required our full attention and care. She was upset and called me a "hard man" with no feelings toward my patients and left the room. I was surprised by her reaction, and Lou's words stayed in my mind for long hours during that night. Had I become a hard person? Has death taken away my sensibilities? Do I see my patients as merely "cases?" I struggled with these questions for most of the night and remembered that I had gone through a similar stage right after my arrival. We humans do not like being confronted with death and react in different ways when it surrounds us, especially when an infant or a child dies. In my case, the load of work during the first months was such that it did not give me the chance to consider the implications of every single death. There were many sick children who might face a similar fate if I did not turn my attention to those who still had some chance.

A few days later, I was able to discuss my own experiences with Lou and how I learned to cope with so many fatalities. I made it clear that there would be more deaths, many of them among children, and that she must be prepared to accept them as part of a cruel reality. In fact, I never got used to see people suffering and dying, especially if they were children. As I closed their eyes, I turned my mind and my heart to those who were still alive, to those who carry the legacy of their deceased brothers and sisters, so that they might continue living through the eyes of those left behind.

A little later Leona Cayser, a nurse and a nationalized Canadian from New Zealand, arrived to replace the untiring and exemplary Carmen Samuels. Repeated episodes of malaria and dysentery had forced Carmen to make her return to the United States before the end of her contract. Finally, in July 1993, seven months after the initiation of the operation, the American Refugee Committee personnel in the Chikwawa district was complete.

NOTES

1. Calderón is a small town in the Ecuador's high Andes, the one locale that specializes in making *masapán* (marzipan), a flour-and-water dough used for shaping figurines.

11

Malawi: Winds of Change

Referendum in Malawi

A few days after the health fair, a milestone took place in the short history of the country: the Referendum of July 14, 1993. Since independence in 1966, as discussed earlier, the only accepted political party was the Malawi Congress Party (MCP), which from that time on had governed the country with a firm hand. After some years of external pressure, Dr. Kamuzu Banda, the president-for-life, finally ceded to this pressure and promised a referendum in which the public would manifest its desire either to continue with a one-party system or to allow competition from alternative political parties, the latter already having the wide support of the population.

For several years various nonofficial parties had presented opposition in a more or less clandestine manner. One party, the Alliance for Democracy (AFORD), with its base and political strength in the northern region of the country, mainly in Tumbuka, was headed by R. Chihana, who had opposed the Banda regime for several de-cades. Chihana, after a long exile in Europe, returned to the country at the end of 1992 and was immediately jailed, remaining there until only a few weeks before the referendum. Another party, the United Democratic Front

(UDF), led by Bakili Muluzi, had wide support in the southern region of the country. The UDF had the largest following among those opposing the MCP. Other parties, although carrying less weight, arose from anonymity and began the struggle to gain sympathizers: the Malawi Democratic Union and the Malawi Democratic Party.

During the previous weeks, we grew accustomed to seeing people raising their hands, and indicating not only the "V" sign for victory but also the unspoken sign for the multiparty system. Although there seemed no doubt that the topic of the referendum was on everyone's mind, there was no guarantee of massive participation. On the day of the election, I woke up early in the morning and went to the local school. Hundreds of men and women were heading toward the election site. As early as 5:00 a.m., voters began forming orderly lines at the little schoolhouse in N'Gona. You could feel the excitement among these people: They were participating for the first time in a democratic process; they were shaping the history of their small country for years to come. President Banda always referred to the Malawians as "my children," even during official speeches. His children were now ready to face their father and challenge his authority. Up to this time they had been living under a tense climate, because there had been rumors that the Young Pioneers, the armed branch of the MCP, would upset the election and cause a voting boycott. For this reason, ARC asked us to prepare a contingency plan to evacuate to Mozambique in case of armed violence, an ironic alternative, considering that Mozambique was not the safest of countries. In spite of the rumors, the referendum was carried out in an atmosphere of tranquillity, and the next day the BBC in London announced a decisive victory for the multiparty system. The government would not acknowledge its defeat until a week later. As soon as the news circulated among the people, there were public demonstrations of joy around the nation. All that remained was to set the date for the first presidential election in the history of Malawi.

To live through the democratic birth of a nation and its first election was a very significant happening for those of us who had the good luck to witness it, and the whole process would culminate in just a few months with the election of the first president to be selected by popular vote. The history of Malawi was to be forever tied to those important events that in the future would determine the role that this small country would play in the convulsing African continent.

CITIES OF MALAWI: BLANTYRE, ZOMBA, AND LILONGWE

It should be evident to the reader by now that a true love for the country and its people was growing within me. Therefore I cannot fail to mention or attempt to describe the principal cities of Malawi, especially one of them, Blantyre. Whoever has had the good fortune to live in this city of 400,000 inhabitants will agree that up to 1994 Blantyre enjoyed the reputation of being one of the most peaceful and tranquil cities in Africa. Surrounded by small hills, this city is the commercial and industrial center of the country. Blantyre was founded in 1876, when an expedition organized by the Free Church of Scotland established a mission in the area inhabited by the Yaos and the Manganjas. The mission took the name of Blantyre in honor of the famous Scottish explorer and missionary David Livingstone, who, upon visiting the area, acknowledged that it reminded him of his birthplace. Later, it became a center of commerce, because of its proximity to the Shire River, although initially the principal trading product was marble. Much later, coffee, sugar, tobacco, and tea products began to dominate commercial trade.

Today, British influences can be seen in the numerous green spaces and gardens throughout this African city. There is not an avenue, a street, or a square that is not covered with acacia trees, jacaranda trees, palms, and a variety of local flowers that all together give the city a picturesque touch. Activities are carried out within a tranquil ambiance, and the vehicular traffic, although heavier than in other populated centers of Malawi, is unobtrusive. Along Victoria Avenue, the principal artery of the city, there is a concentration of banks, commercial centers, and businesses. The black, green, and red of the Malawian flag waves from all the public buildings as well as from many private ones, and the official photo of President Kamuzu Hastings Banda used to be seen in the entrance of practically all the buildings. The tallest buildings are no more than ten stories and only a few reach that height. Two-story buses run through the streets of Blantyre, recalling the former British presence. Well-to-do African families and the international community live in the residential sector, in large houses of typical British architecture, with wide gardens and lots of green spaces. In spite of being hot in Blantyre, the climate never reaches the infernal temperatures of the Lower Shire zone, the seat of one of the refugee camps under my supervision. However, until the middle of this century, it was common among European expatriates to move to Zomba in order to avoid the months of oppressive heat.

Not everything is green and comfortable though, as some areas at a distance away from the city center are shantytowns or "townships" inhabited totally by black people with scant resources. In these, over-crowding, lack of facilities for drinking water and electricity, insalubrity, and neglect are the most notable characteristics. Until 1994, Malawi was considered an eminently rural country with only fifteen percent of the population living in urban areas, and urban growth was not as excessive as in dozens of Latin American cities. In Blantyre toward the end of 1993, it was rare to find beggars on the streets, in spite of Malawi's being one of the poorest countries on the planet. Banda discouraged rural immigration, and his henchmen took beggars from the streets, so that the president would not see any sign of inadequate political distribution of wealth. Later, with the opening of a new democratic process, the rural population began to turn its eyes to the city as a fountain of work and of satisfaction for immediate necessities—including basic health care needs—that were not covered at the traditional village level, resulting in an increased number of unemployed people wandering the streets, as the urban centers could not cope with the demand for work. However, it is interesting to refer to studies, which demonstrate that immigrants obtain better health coverage in urban settings than in rural ones.

Paul Basch, in his book *International Health,* describes immigrants living in cities as having lower mortality rates than rural inhabitants, perhaps because they have better access to health care and sanitation services.

Blantyre is far from being considered a metropolis. There are only a few restaurants and two theaters. In order to mitigate these limitations on entertainment, the population highly depends on get-togethers in the homes of family or friends. The Sports Club of Blantyre is a country club for the elite to which the majority of the white community belongs as well as those few Africans in favorable economic circumstances. The club has a very British orientation, with a golf course, tennis and squash courts, and fields for cricket and rugby. Until just a few years ago, only whites could elect to hold membership there; not even well to do Hindus were qualified. Invitations to dine at the club were very common among the international community, and they were traded around indefinitely, which created an atmosphere of contagious hospitality.

The city of Zomba, the ancient capital of Malawi and the seat of Parliament, dates from 1885 when Consulate Hawes chose the site as the seat of his administration. Zomba is a charming but small city located in the folds of the hills of the same name that form a plateau that rises 6900 feet (2100 meters) in altitude. This city of 53,000 inhabitants maintains the characteristic features of an African locality, having a dynamic market and adding a young population composed for the most part of students at the University of Zomba. The verdure and the relative freshness of the area contrast with other regions of the country that are poor in vegetation and excessively hot. Zomba is a university city with a large academic population, among them some British and some North American professors. This city and its plateau were to become my favorite spots for relaxation, especially after having met Dr. Mitchel Strumpf, a New York musicologist who had resided in Malawi for more than a decade. Mitch presided over the active Musical Society of Zomba, a group of musicians and friends of music from every race and social condition. Once a month, the society gave a concert, each time in a different house, to which all were invited, especially if one played some musical instrument. It was in this environment where I became an honorary member of the society and where—in the company of the excellent French musician, and my great friend, Ricardo García— we enjoyed nights of music and Bohemia.

Climbs up to Zomba Plateau, whether on foot or in a vehicle, never failed to awaken in me a sense of peace and harmony, especially after living for several consecutive weeks in the refugee camps. The humid semitropical atmosphere plus the freshness of the air at such heights are the precise remedy for an oppressed spirit. Giant ferns, limpid waterfalls, woods of pine, and rare species of brilliantly colored orchids give the sensation of being in a dream that is interrupted only by the howls of the mandrills and the monkeys that balance themselves in the tops of the acacia trees. There are several cottages for lodging atop the plateau. Both the United States and the British embassies have their own cottages, which they rent to their functionaries during the summer weekends and holidays. During the nights, the temperature drops considerably, being a good time to light a fire in the fireplace and to let oneself become enraptured by the silence and peace of the mountain.

Lilongwe, today the capital of the country and the seat of all the ministries and accredited embassies in Malawi, was conceived as a project in 1969, coming into reality in 1972, the year of the first phase of completion. Lilongwe, located in the central region, was designed as a garden city, where the centralized government would try to balance the existing disparity with the southern region, the location of the majority of the country's population and resources. In 1994, the population of Lilongwe reached 220,000 inhabitants, thus, following Blantyre, becoming the second most populated city in Malawi. It has been catalogued as "a city without character," as have other carefully planned cities (e.g., Brasilia). Through my relationship with Conny Arvis, a functionary of the United States Embassy, I had the opportunity on several occasions to stay in the city. Lilongwe was not designed with the local population in mind: The locals greatly lack for vehicles and were obliged to cross-enormous distances on foot, unable to afford public transportation. In addition, the public system does not cover all the routes. The international community and the local fauna enjoy the enormous green spaces more than the Malawians do. One night, in one of those spacious greens near Conny's residence, we watched at close range a medium-size feline— not identifiable for the darkness—that was marauding the area, possibly in search of food. That was near downtown Lilongwe.

Malawian cities have few places of interest along the museum trail. Among those few however, there is the Museum of Malawi in Blantyre, which exhibits pieces of historic, archeological, and anthropological interest. The Zomba War Memorial, erected in memory of the soldiers of the Royal African Company of Rifles who fell during the First World War, and the cemetery of Zomba, which encompasses the tombs of fifty-four soldiers killed during the two world wars, are some of the monuments to be found in the country. Nevertheless, there is no doubt that the places of major attraction are the national parks, with their variety of wild fauna and flora, and Lake Malawi with its renowned beaches. Safaris in Liwonde, Nyika, and Vwaza are worthy of consideration. However, I still believe that Malawi's major asset is its people. The gentle manners and generosity of the average Malawian are well known in the region, and on more than one occasion I was honored to be a guest of local friends from N'Gona, who shared with me their simple but meaningful meals, which often ended with the traditional story-telling that I loved so much.

It takes years to be able to take in the essence of Malawi; to be able to understand the idiosyncrasies of its people and therefore to understand fully its multiple problems. On one occasion, I became quite irritated listening to the monologue of a North American colleague who had worked for three weeks as a volunteer surgeon in the Queen Elizabeth Hospital in Blantyre. According to him, in those few days he had become an expert on questions of health, with a series of answers for all the grave health problems of the country. This attitude was repeated by

101

several technical consultants who had come to countries of the so-called Third World, believing they knew everything and ignoring or undervaluing the local personnel, who, while indeed qualified, failed to fulfill the fundamental requisite: to be born or to come from a developed nation.

INTERNATIONAL HEALTH AND TECHNICAL COOPERATION

The situation described above is repeated in many parts of the world where technical cooperation is needed. It brings us to the question of the concept or definition of international health. In his 1992 report, Charles Godue[1] proposes four basic categories of concepts of international health: (1) the "Germs Do Not Respect Borders" category; (2) the "International Health is the Health of the Poor" category; (3) the "Functionalism in International Health" category; and (4) the international health as a component of international relations and a foreign policy tool category.

The first category is a simplistic approach in which the authors acknowledge the fact that infectious diseases and other health hazards—such as pollutants—cross national boundaries. However, this concept fails to recognize other factors directly related to the transmission or prevention of health hazards across the border such as social, economic, and political issues.

The second category of concepts limits international health to public health initiatives of developed countries directed at the poor in developing countries. The volunteer physician I was forced to listen to for a long time would agree very much with this concept, although it has some major flaws: It is unidimensional, for it assumes that international health activities are exclusively in the realm of biomedical public health; it is unidirectional, for it assumes that disease moves only in one direction from developing to developed nations, and it assumes that local professionals have little or nothing to contribute to the process of understanding and/or controlling the variety of factors involved. To support this argument I must relate my own experience: I have good reason to believe that upon my arrival, some of my colleagues were not too happy to see a doctor from a developing country coming to assume a health coordination position in Malawi. My master's degree from the University of Illinois in Chicago did help to provide some assurance of my qualifications, although the School of Public Health did not prepare me enough in certain critical areas of international health such as technical cooperation.

The third category defends the leadership of international organizations in relations between nations searching for regional integration. In other words, the state is sovereign in relation to international health issues, and if that involves threats to the health situation of populations in different countries, the international organizations should take charge.

The fourth and final category considers international health as a component of international relations and a foreign policy tool. As an example, we could cite the cholera epidemic initiated in Peru and how it triggered a series of events that fall within the health field as well as in the international relations domain. Ulisses Paniset, an international health expert, believes that there is a current lack of a clearly delineated international health theory, and that this lack "hinders the development of an international health statecraft, a set of policy proposals for health and development issues to serve as a decision-making guide at the high level or for international organizations."

There were numerous international organizations carrying out activities in Malawi and Mozambique, with hundreds of experts from different parts of the world—mainly from developed countries—working in technical cooperation. International technical cooperation at its most basic level can be defined as the process by which two or more international parties work together to achieve specific objectives. According to the Pan American Health Organization, technical cooperation does not merely involve the transfer of knowledge and resources from those who have to those who have not. It should be viewed as a mutual teaching-learning process in which both parties benefit from the experience.[2] The Netherlands government was funding several health projects in Malawi, and at the same time it was providing technical cooperation by sending physicians to support the work-loaded clinical and administrative local staff. In fact, these young doctors were providing much needed specialized health care to a country lacking in health professionals. After spending a few months at the Regional Hospital, they would be sent to district hospitals in the interior, where they had to take over administrative duties, for which they were not formally trained, nevertheless acquiring in the process valuable on-the-job experience. Some of them would be appointed as district health officers (DHOs) and even regional health officers (RHOs). The Dutch RHO for the southern region was appointed to such a high position after only a few years working in the country, something unthinkable for those few Malawians who struggled through medical school and who did not have the right connections in the MCP party. This European professional in his early thirties could hardly have imagined reaching a level just below that of the minister of health if he were in his native country. In fact, Malawi was providing a precious experience to young Dutch doctors who would eventually return to Europe to offer their expertise to their national health systems. Some might continue to pursue degrees in public health or in health administration.

However, technical cooperation implies full participation of the locals, and in Malawi this seldom happened. In most cases, the NGOs or bilateral agencies came with their own idea of what the country or the refugees needed and proceeded to implement their programs after obtaining authorization from government officials who saw in this assistance the possibility of allocating some resources to rural areas that they could not cover with their own limited budget. There was no coordinated effort to establish the extent of the cooperation or to define areas of cooperation; in some cases two or more NGOs were duplicating activities in the same region. ARC was one of the few NGOs that hired local health professionals with broad experience in the local and national level. By the end of the year, several of the nurses working for ARC in the two camps were Malawians as was the health coordinator at the main office, Mrs. Martha Gunda, to whom I was to report. However, I should point out that health professionals were hard to find, and this was one of the reasons the process in Malawi was more likely to be one of technical aid or assistance than true technical cooperation. Moreover, the presence of hundreds of thousands of Mozambican refugees diverted a substantial portion of the foreign aid, having at a certain point a large number of the international organizations based in Malawi working in refugee programs. This situation became a policy issue that reached the presidential level, adding a different dimension to the process of technical cooperation that falls in the last of the categories described above, which considers international health as a component of international relations and a foreign policy tool.

KAMUZU ACADEMY

Known as the "Eton of Africa," Kamuzu Academy is the most important secondary school in Malawi. Founded by President Banda in 1977 and opened in 1981, the school is located near Mtunthama, the village where it is believed that Banda was born, Mtunthama, some eighteen miles (thirty kilometers) to the east of Kasungu. Following the traditions and features of the best secondary boarding schools of Britain, Kamuzu Academy takes into its classrooms the best students from all the districts throughout the country; students coming as much from the urban sectors as from the smaller rural villages.

The reason this center for secondary learning interested me and why I wanted to describe it, is not to sing the virtues that of course it has, but to detail the anachronisms and contradictions that have made way for a growing sentiment of opposition against some practices that have occurred within its walls. For a start, from the moment the student enters the academy, he is categorically prohibited from communicating in Chichewa, the official language of the county after English, forced to speak exclusively in the latter language. All the professors come from outside of the country, especially from Great

Britain and the United States, since, as Banda said, "There is no African teacher yet born worthy of giving classes in my Academy." As part of the study program, great value is given to the study of the Latin and Greek classics, while the study of history is limited to the West, eliminating Africa. The loyalty of the government party, the MCP, must be blind to the fact that in its classrooms there is no place for political discussion, let alone the question of governmental actions.

I wonder what kind of individual Banda was trying to fashion in his academy. Perhaps people who would think and act like westerners in an African setting? Blind followers of a dictatorial regime that extols the virtues of an unquestionable leader blotted with power? Happily, in the first democratic elections of May 1994, the public threw out Banda's life-long political pretensions, and his followers, and placed their vote of confidence in the hands of Bakili Muluzi, the current president of Malawi. As late as my return to Ecuador in 1994, the future of the Kamuzu Academy was still being discussed, most people believing that it will finally be closed and that the beautiful building will either be sold or converted to a luxury hotel. However, it seems to me that the most acceptable option is to maintain the school as a center for secondary learning, but to completely revise the curricula and to totally re-evaluate its objectives. I would venture to lean toward this last option, confident that in the not too distant future the students who graduate from Kamuzu Academy will be of a pan-African conscience, committed to the national reality, with a mind open to dialogue and opposition—if worthy—and with a true vision of the potential that can be generated in the youth of Malawi.

NOTES
1. See Charles Godue. *International Health: A North South Debate* (Washington DC: Pan American Health Organization, PAHO/WHO, 1992).
2. *Rethinking International Technical Cooperation in Health*, (Washington DC: Pan American Health Organization, PAHO/WHO, 1996).

12

MUSIC AND ART

The purpose of this book is not to go into great detail about the variety of artistic expression in this part of the world. However, during my almost two years in Africa, I could not fail to notice time and again the importance of dance and music in the daily life there. As I have described earlier, these cultural expressions are not only utilized toward a social end, but their role also includes a therapeutic objective, as in the case of the Vimbuza or the Mashawe dances. I will continue to describe some of the occasions on which I was, directly or indirectly, involuntarily related to some matter of art and how these occasions influenced the work I was doing.

N'YAO DANCERS

The first time I saw the famous dancers of the N'Yao Kulewanku Secret Society was in the camp at Kunyinda not long after my arrival. Upon hearing the sound of the drums, my curiosity drew me to one of the sections of the camp where there seemed to be a traditional ceremony in progress. Noticing my presence, the spectators who were enjoying the rhythmic cadence of the drums led me to a place of honor in a circle they had formed. After a few minutes a group of individuals appeared whose faces were completely covered by human- and animal-like masks or by feathers. Their athletic bodies were clothed with loincloths made of multicolored strips of some vegetable fiber. They were the N'Yao Dancers. The same type of decoration hung from their ankles, knees, and arms for the purpose of emphasizing their movements during the dance. Along with them were several individuals armed with dried branches, frightening the children who watched the dancers' footsteps with great curiosity. Others shook bells or tambourines, which seemed to communicate instructions to the dancers who responded with guttural sounds or howls that seemed to come from wild animals.

One by one the dancers made their entrance in what seemed like a competition. Complementing the rhythm of the drums and encouraged by the growing in intensity, the participants made a show of their attributes and were recompensed first with applause and later with money from the spectators who threw coins when the dance reached its peak. The dance itself was rapid, full of energy and movement; the dancers' feet raised the dust because of the rapidity with which they executed their complex steps. During the whole time the drumming never ceased, and when some percussionist grew tired, someone else substituted for him with a renewed vigor that took up the contagious rhythm. A women's chorus accompanied the dancers to the climax until one of the dancers fell exhausted, and just at that moment a new N'Yao dancer made his entrance only to reinitiate the cycle. As the spectacle continued for hours, I had to withdraw, after having tossed sufficient coins to keep the group happy.

While in the camp at Chang'ambika, I had the opportunity to establish contact with the leader of the N'Yao group, and after that, his dancers participated in a series of health-related events such as the health fair and the closure of the training seminars for the local health personnel. This was how I learned more about this secret organization—its origins in the tribal community having begun many centuries ago—which, according to K. Chiromo in his study on the visual arts of Malawi, "fills the gap between the prehistoric era and modernism." I should point out that it was a difficult job to obtain information about the initiation rites and ceremonies and the preparation of the men. Chiromo explains that according to the traditions of this sect, the N'Yao is the personification of spirits and for that reason their language is not human. A man becomes a N'Yao only after passing an unrevealed initiation; then he must learn the secret tongue they use to communicate among themselves, especially during the dance ceremonies, which is based on gestures and guttural sounds difficult to identify. Before beginning the dance, the N'Yao chews certain roots or drinks some concoction that "transforms" him and permits him to communicate with the humanoid or animal spirits that he represents. He begins his frenetic dance in a state of trance that lasts until he is completely worn out, and falls down. Another dancer takes his place. The out-going dancer takes himself off to rest in a traditional construction set apart from the place of celebration, where no one but the N'Yao may be present. This little stockade must be built each time the dancers perform, and it fills the twofold role of secreting the dancer from curious onlookers, while enhancing the mystery that envelops these personalities.

BLACK PASELI: MALAWI'S PIONEER OF POPULAR MUSIC

It was during a visit to Zomba when the Musical Society gave its monthly concert, that I had the opportunity to meet and hear an individual of more than seventy years of age who delighted the whole audience with his own melodies that had sprung from the very soul of the Malawian people. This musical septuagenarian, known as Black Paseli, suffered from the same metamorphosis that any true artist undergoes in changing from being rather reserved personally to being able to face and captivate an audience with a musical instrument in hand on stage. The energy that emanated from this otherwise weary body was contagious, and the notes of the song that would become one of my favorites, "Napolo," flowed clearly and melodiously. In spite of the years, his voice denoted the strength of a creative spirit and in Chichewa, the language of his grandparents, described in a poetic manner the disaster of the terrible flood of 1946 in Zomba, which is remembered by the name Napolo. My interest in this character grew, and it was Mitchel Strumpf, the North American musicologist now rooted in Malawi, who furnished me with more details about the life of this musical pioneer. At the same time I found several articles written about his work.

Black Paseli was born in 1921 in a little village near Zomba, Mlumbe, and he learned to play the guitar that belonged to a Britisher for whom he worked. Together with his brother, Barry, he founded a group that traveled to various regions of central Africa. In 1947, Paseli became the first Malawian to record his own compositions, which brought him fame not only in Malawi but also in Zambia, in South Africa, and in what today is Zimbabwe. For years he was an example to younger generations as someone who had made inroads into the world of popular African music.

On several other occasions, I was to have the pleasure of hearing Black Paseli, and he always happily consented to please me with his interpretation of "Napolo." It surprised me that Mitch always went to pick up Paseli at least five hours before the time of the performance. During this long wait, I took the opportunity to learn more about this popular songwriter who patiently awaited the hour of the beginning of the recital in Dr. Strumpf's house. Upon asking him about this perhaps excessive waiting period, Mitch answered that something Paseli had never learned to value was punctuality; therefore, it would be nothing strange for Black Paseli, on some weekend, to give in to the request of some friend that he attend some tribal fiesta, where they would sing and drink beer into the early morning hours, without remembering for even a single moment that he had already made another promise for that day. In order to avoid these situations and valuing punctuality—like a good westerner—he preferred to keep Paseli under his thumb during the hours before a concert.

A CONCERT TO BENEFIT THE REFUGEES

For several months, Lou and I had been coming to the aid of various community and sports activities in both refugee camps, which included, among others, the creation of a clothing fund for the children in the Intensive Nutritional Center, the creation of a children's recreation center, and the sponsorship of soccer teams in both camps. Not much later I found out it would be necessary to have a better and more effective strategy in order to assure the continuation of these recreational activities since they involved significant expense. At the beginning, the above-mentioned actions were financed with money from our own pockets, but we soon understood that there had to be another way to get money to finance those little programs. Music immediately presented itself as a major and most agreeable alternative. Furthermore, the idea of playing together with a guitarist like Ricardo García, the French-Spanish musician whose ability with the guitar was impressive, was another motivation for bringing about a concert to benefit the refugees in the Chikwawa district camps. The auditorium of the French Cultural Center in Blantyre was the chosen spot, as it offered the best facilities. During three consecutive weekends a small group assembled that included, besides Ricardo and I, the excellent African percussionist Isaac Nyerenda; my friend and interpreter of the guitar Bashir Sacranie; and Aaron Sangala, a Malawian friend of mine who with a few intense lessons learned to play two tunes in the Andean charango.

A few days before the recital I got the idea of including slides of Ecuador. And so it was that African, European, and American eyes enjoyed the images of my beloved Ecuador, while the notes of the Andean music flowed for the first time in these latitudes: we played the *pasillo*[1] "Invernal" (Winter) as a picture of colonial Quito was presented in the frame, the *Sanjuanito* "Longuita" accompanied the majestic Chimborazo; and the beat of the rondador the Inca fort of Ingapirca. The sound of the rondador, along with that of the quena, charango, and

111

zampoñas took hold of the audience and transported them to a previously unknown land.

The concert was free, but we placed a gratuity box at the entrance of the auditorium. Through the sale of cassettes of my music and the generous contributions received that night, we were able to create a fund that would last for several months to purchase clothes for the undernourished children admitted to the INC in the two camps, as well as a fund for the Soccer School for Children in Chang'ambika that functioned up to the closing of the camp. The concert was so highly praised and commented upon that during the following months we had to repeat the performance in Zomba and in Lilongwe, each with the same success.

NOTES
1. *Pasillo* and *Sanjuanito* are traditional Ecuadorian rhythms.

13

A DREAM TO SAVOR

NORTHERN BOUND

An idea came up during a chat with my Argentinean friend, Dr. Guillermo Bertoletti, that we take a trip together to the north, especially to the Nyika National Park. A break came at the most opportune time, when, at last, Lou Cooney arrived at the Chang'ambika camp. Also, it was an opportunity to enjoy a well-earned rest after the hard work of creating the health fair. My new travel companion was a real character, and he proved it from the day of his arrival in Malawi. Defying the "dress code" that forbade men to have long hair, he managed to hide his last- minute-made pony tail under his shirt. The customs official, undoubtedly used to this kind of trick, was charmed by the eloquence of Guillermo, who wasted no time in attracting the attention of this and other Malawian officials with his loud voice, heavy English accent, and broad and contagious smile. He was allowed into the country with his long hair and dense beard untouched.

In a short time his humorous spirit and openness towards the refugees in the three camps under his supervision made him a respected, but more importantly, a well-liked member of the MSF health team. I will always remember Guillermo's support during the cholera epidemic, when he loaned us vital supplies to treat our patients during the time the muddy roads made it impossible for the ARC truck to deliver the much-needed intravenous and oral rehydration solutions to the Chang'ambika camp. I will always be grateful for the MSF hospitality in Mwanza when the road, weather, or security conditions did not allow me to continue on to my camp. Moreover, I doubt the refugees will forget the many occasions when Guillermo himself carried a sick baby in his strong arms to the hospital after exhausting all the available resources in the local health unit. I am quite sure they will remember him running towards the crowd to celebrate the scoring of the victory goal against my team during the soccer match we played against each other. Deep within me I also celebrated that score, for I was witnessing the communion of this man with the people that he served.

June 1993

I see him taking off his shirt in exultation and throwing it to the crowd who could now see the scars in his broad back, those signs of torture that he kept as a silent reminder of the atrocities committed during the years of the Dirty War in Argentina. The refugees shared their own pain and sorrow with a man who had experienced persecution himself and who had had to flee his own country for several years. They laughed tears of joy because suffering has a way of marking people forever, so that later they can recognize each other and they can share in silence feelings of empathy that go beyond the material perception. I can still hear his thunderous, not too harmonic voice singing the zamba[1] "Valderrama" or the Peronist Party anthem with his left hand raised over his shoulder and his right hand holding a beer: "Con el fusil en la mano...."

His loud and contagious laugh announced or denounced him wherever he went, his voice turning suddenly serious when the refugee issue came into the discussion; he would then become a passionate advocate for the rights of his refugees. That is my friend, a man in love with life, whose struggle against injustice will continue forever and wherever the road takes him.

The idea of the trip to the north crystallized at the end of July, and we began our journey at Mwanza; after the first day of driving we stopped at Lilongwe, the capital of Malawi, where we stayed with the only representatives of Bolivia in the country. The Quiroga family showed us the famed Latin American hospitality, and they truly made us feel welcome. The following morning, we continued the long journey in our trusty Toyota Land Cruiser in which we would cross the northern and central regions of the country. Besides the dozens of little villages that we passed, we went through Kasungu, a city 90 miles (140 kilometers) north of Lilongwe; Mzuzu, the principal city of the northern region; and Rumphi, more than 490 miles (780 kilometers) from our point of departure. In a day and a half we had crossed from south to north, almost the entire country. However, the trip was not finished, and only after an hour of traveling on a dirt road did we arrive at Thazima gate, the entrance to Nyika National Park. From there we continued on another 35 miles (56 kilometers) to Chelinda camp where we were hoping to find accommodations, although we had not made reservations. As we thought might happen, darkness fell, which leant a touch of adventure to this trip through the unknown. The stillness of the night was broken by the crossing of several zebras only a few feet in front of our vehicle, a very exciting event, since it was the first time I had seen these beautiful equines in their natural habitat.

Arriving at a crossroad, we read a sign announcing another lodging, but located in neighboring Zambia. Two countries share the Nyika Mesa, and for its closer proximity we decided to look for lodging in this refuge. A few minutes after crossing the invisible frontier we arrived at the rest house, only to find it empty and closed. The Chelinda camp in Malawi was the only viable alternative, and so we continued our journey. It was already well into the night when we arrived. The whole shelter was in total silence, and we could not make out even a single employee. We were beginning to get worried when we found what seemed to be the main cabin from which the only source of light was emanating. We went in and settled ourselves in front of the fireplace, as it had become very cold. Hunger overcame prudence, and we decided to roast the meat that we had bought in Mzuzu, using the coals in the fireplace. After a little while, an employee arrived who asked us if we had a reservation. To our negative response, he informed us that there was no room available. We must have shown little sign of wanting to leave, since at that hour, 11 p.m., we had no other option for lodging, and we made it clear that our intention was to spend the night right there in the middle of the guest lobby. I think it was our attitude that in the end helped him remember that there was one cabin available, and he took us to it immediately. Inside we found hot water, a kitchen, and comfortable beds, where we quickly laid our tired bodies.

Chelinda, an accommodation belonging to the Department of National Parks of Malawi, is comprised of a series of wooden mountain cabins, the center one being the largest and functioning as lobby, dining room, and kitchen. There is a little electric generator that runs for a few hours at night. After 9 p.m. darkness takes over, and only kerosene lamps break the monotony. They use wood fire to heat the water, which is carried in ducts to the shower in each cabin. All this allows for the almost unaltered magic of the place, fully enjoying the contact with nature. Travelers must bring in their own food, but there is a local cook who will prepare and serve meals.

The Nyika Plateau, one of the most beautiful highlands on the continent, covers an area of 1,158 square miles (3,000 square kilometers) and spreads across two countries, Zambia and Malawi. It is a high zone that in certain sectors can rise to more than 6,300 feet (2,000 meters) above sea level and the site of Malawi's second highest elevation, Nganda. The flora is varied, with numerous species of flowers; the most famous—the orchid—is catalogued as having up to 120 varieties. There are majestic juniper forests that grow on the southeast part of the mesa. Little hills abound in this zone where herds of elland, antelopes, and zebras graze. Between November and May, it is possible to witness a singular spectacle, for it's the time of birthing for the leopards which can be observed with their newborn cubs, some only a few weeks old. The next morning, with the aid of map and compass, we set off on a trip that would be full of excitement and surprises. Luck was with us, for we had the opportunity to see close-up a variety of local fauna: antelopes, kudus (a kind of large antelope), wild boar, jackals, wild dogs, Burchell zebras, etc. The almost total absence of other human beings made us feel like a part of the wildlife of the area. We went to various high points, where we could admire the plains that stretched to the west and that made up a part of Zambia. At night, in the company of an armed guard, we went in search of the area's great predator, the leopard. Unfortunately, on that night it wasn't possible to see that beautiful animal, the terror of the local fauna.

The next day we reassumed our journey to our next objective, the Vwaza Wildlife Reserve. The map showed an entrance to the extreme north, much closer than the one on the southeast side. It was an adventure crossing the seldom-used roads, and on several occasions we found ourselves forced to use our limited Chichewa in order to get directions. After taking several detours we arrived at the famous entrance only to read the announcement that the route was closed because of poor road conditions. With a very South American resignation, we went back to the first crossroads, determined to cover the additional 25 miles (40 kilometers) to get to the main entrance. After hours of travel, we arrived at our destination, and in only a few minutes the landscape in front of us convinced us that it had been worth the effort.

The camp at the reserve consisted of some rustic straw cabins that covered the canvas tents, and inside there were cots from which the infallible mosquito netting and the kerosene lamps were hanging. These cabins looked out on a lake a third of a mile (some 500 meters) away, where antelopes and hippopotamus refreshed themselves from the noonday heat. The absence of guides was resolved when Guillermo decided to place in plain view a crate of beer that we had bought along the way; soon, Francis Phiri, a Malawian park guard, was right there, ready to accompany us in our search for wild elephants.

This zone is one of the areas still inhabited by the feared tsetse fly, the carrier of *Trypanosoma rhodesiense*, the parasite that causes the "sleeping sickness," so called because in its most advanced stages it produces, somnolence, body wasting, and weakness; signs of involvement of the central nervous system. Without proper treatment, this type of trypanosomiasis can be lethal in a matter of weeks or months. One survey taken in villages located in the swampy region of Vwaza showed that 4.2 percent of the population had the parasite in their bodies. The parasites do not only affect humans. We have often seen portrayals of early safaris with a long line of porters carrying a box on their head, but we failed to ask ourselves why no animals were carrying these burdens: They simply did not survive. Paul Basch describes the importance of the sleeping sickness as an "inhibitor of economic development." The introduction of large animals for food, labor, or transportation in many areas of the continent has been prohibited because of the presence of *Trypanosoma rhodesiense* for fear the animals may fall victims to *nagana*, the animal version of African sleeping sickness. The introduction of the disease to east Africa—where it was unknown until late last century—is attributed to the Stanley expedition from the Congo area to the east African lake region, which resulted in a terrible outbreak among residents of Uganda from 1900 to 1908. The death toll exceeded 200,000 people, all because of an insect that was flying freely inside a car.... If it did happen, it would not be the first time that westerns—through direct or indirect actions—introduced a devastating disease in areas where it never occurred before, causing death and sickness among the locals.

Again, luck was on our side, as a few minutes into the trip our guide caught sight of a herd of thirty to thirty-five elephants. We got out of the vehicle and moved within some 70 feet (20 meters) away from them, where the cameras did their job. The African elephant is the largest of the land animals, approaching 11 feet (3.5 meters) in height and 6 tons in weight. While the elephants of Vwaza, unlike those of the Liwonde Park in the south of the country, are not known for their aggressiveness, it is always advisable to maintain one's distance, as our guide Phiri never stopped reminding us. It was exciting to see those pachyderms in their own natural surrounding. The leader of the herd was suddenly bothered by our close-ness, and he made movements and sounds that assured us of his vexation, for which we took our respective cam-eras and got ourselves out of there. Phiri seemed to sharpen his vision each time he finished a beer, locating wild life in the most concealed places. Returning to the car, he offered to take us to a very special place in the Vwaza Reserve, to the site of the confluence of the rivers.

Because of the partially dry bed of the Vwaza, one of the two rivers, we could take the vehicle close to the con-fluence, where we left it to continue on foot. A group of approximately thirty hippopotamus were playing in the muddy water, looking altogether like a rocky island in movement. Our proximity did not seem important to them until we were barely 50 feet (15 meters) away, and then hippopotamus "island" vanished. The hippopotamus, or river horse, is a distant relative of the pig and rivals the great Indian rhinoceros as the second largest living land animal. It reaches 13 feet (4.2 meters) in length and almost 5 feet (1.5 meters) high. Its weight can reach 4 tons. There is a thick layer of fat underneath the skin, from whose pores is secreted a rosy colored oily fluid known as "pink sweat" that lubricates the skin of the ani-mal. The canine tusks measure 30 inches (0.76 meters) in length and occasionally exceed 60 inches (1.52 meters), including the long root encased in the gum. One of the gifts that I was to receive later was from a native friend who had carved the entire outer face of a hippopotamus canine tusk with the images of African flora and fauna. A hippopotamus herd has 20 to 100 members. The central area of a territory is reserved for females and the young, and surrounding it are other areas, each occupied by adult males. Contrary to long held beliefs, a female is the leader of the herd. The yawn that characterizes them is not related to sleepiness or to boredom; it is an aggressive gesture, a threat made before a fight.

After a short walk following the water's edge, we came to the confluence of the two rivers, a place that conserves the wild landscape that must have covered a large part of the continent before man left his destructive footprint. Acacia trees and cottonwoods—or, as they are known in Africa, the baobab—break the monotony of the panorama, with only our human presence disturbing the savage equilibrium. We had a small fright when a lone hippopotamus that had been underwater came up when it heard us passing nearby and suddenly came charging toward our group. It seems it only was trying to frighten us, which it succeeded in doing, because when it got to the edge of the water it turned around to dive back in.

After almost two hours of hiking we returned to the vehicle, and on the return route to the camp we came across a herd of approximately 200 African cape buffalo, which have the reputation of being the most dangerous of the African wild animals. They can reach 4.9 feet (1.5 meters) in height, and the adult males weigh almost one ton. The horns can attain a span of more than 4 feet (1.2 meters). In late afternoon we were able to spot kudus and other varieties of antelopes. The day was far from over because back in our tent, just before dark, we decided to watch the elephants from close quarters while they quenched their thirst in the nearby lake. I was the first to go, but after thirty minutes without seeing even one footprint of these giants, I returned to camp. Guillermo, armed with his camera, a lantern, and the ever-present beer, went off to the lake to try his luck. A few moments passed, and soon the elephants made their triumphal entrance. Meanwhile, I had not seen any sign of my crazy Argentinean companion. The forest-keepers were overcome with fear, expecting the worst. So when it grew dark, I decided to go in search of my friend. Several minutes passed without finding any sign of Guillermo, when suddenly I saw a light coming through the tree branches. In just a few moments my traveling companion and I were back together again, because he was signaling me with his lantern from his unique vantagepoint. High up in the crown of an acacia tree, drinking a Carlsberg beer, he was enjoying the broad panorama from his strategic position. I soon joined him, swathed by the tree, since the elephants were still hanging about the place.

Back in camp, to the relief of the forest-keepers, we got ready to enjoy the dinner that the local cook prepared. That magical evening, complete with wine, we took cover under the mantel of Alpha Centaur and the Southern Cross, in a night so clear that it reminded me of Lake Garzacocha in the Amazonia in Ecuador. Seated before our improvised fire, it was not difficult to imagine myself as an explorer of the past century in this virgin land, where once another doctor, David Livingstone, sat dreaming before a fire.

To savor dreams as they are happening is one a part of the daily aspects of learning to live. I believe that I'm not far from the truth when I say that during my walks in Nyika and Vwaza I knew I was fabricating a dream that I would remember forever.

NOTES

1. Zamba is a popular Argentinean rhythm.

14

MINES AND MINEFIELDS

THE HEAVIEST MINED AREA OF MOZAMBIQUE

August 29, 1993

"The visitor is someone important, and he wants to speak with you immediately," repeated Domingo, one of my aides. I was completely engrossed in my work in the medical consulting room at the Kunyinda camp. We were experiencing more tranquil times since the recent epidemics that had been wearing down the refugee camps were now either controlled or had subsided because of the dry season. Our priorities were now directed to the area of development and community health, with an important component being health education and training for health personnel. The work, which did not cease being arduous, had become less suffocating than in the first months.

Major Patrick Lewis, a commander of the RENAMO Forces (National Resistance of Mozambique) for the Mutarara district in Mozambique, was heading the delegation of guerrillas who had come across the frontier to the Kunyinda refugee camp with a mission completely different from those violent ones that he had recently been carrying out along the border between Malawi and Mozambique. This time it was a mission in search of humanitarian support from ARC. In this way a meeting was begun in which the representative from RENAMO described the current health situation and the immediate needs of the Doa population in the Mutarara district in Mozambique. Following that, he made a formal petition for material and technical assistance in order to ameliorate the grave situation that was, according to him, claiming lives daily. He mentioned problems such as an almost total lack of the most elemental medication and medical supplies, the immediate need to rebuild the health station, the dangerous lack of water, and the presence of mines in vast areas of the sector. During the meeting, Major Patrick presented himself as a person who could handle difficult problems in times of peace as well as he probably had in time of war.

After explaining to him that aid of any type would be channeled to him only after an evaluation visit to the area, Major Patrick affirmed that the invitation was open, and that no delegation had come before because no organization showed any interest or the determination to visit the area considered dangerous because of the presence of antipersonnel mines in wide sectors of the district. "The road from Kunyinda already is open," he told us, assuring us that they knew about the dangerous areas that should be avoided, thereby minimizing any risk. For better security, I asked him and his assistant to accompany us in our vehicle during the trip, a request he accepted. The date was set for the August 25, 1993.

Alfred M'Hone (the ARC health assistant for Kunyinda), Commandant Patrick, his field aide, our chauffeur Noel M'Kandawire, and I began the trip early in the morning, striking out on a local road that was not necessarily constructed for the passage of vehicles, even for small ones. Crossing the frontier would have gone unnoticed by the ARC

team had it not been for one stop where the guerrillas reclaimed the arms they left in a hut. The
route became progressively more wooded as we penetrated Mozambique, which was quite interesting,
because only a few miles back, in neighboring
Malawi, there were very few trees to be seen, and
deforestation had risen to critical levels. The rural
African population uses firewood almost exclusively
as a source of energy. In a situation of human con-
glomeration, as is the case in a refugee camp, the
encircling areas suffer the effects of deforestation.
In Malawi, where more than one million refugees
were counted up to 1992, the ecological situation
of the frontier areas with Mozambique—the site of
the majority of the refugee camps—was seriously
affected, forcing the authorities and international
organizations to take joint actions. ARC was active
in environmental issues and currently supporting
a tree nursery project in Kunyinda to reforest the
areas surrounding the two refugee camps.

These trees and thickets were only a few yards
away from each other, and yellow grass covered
nearly the entire area. Limestone and other hard
rocks of various sizes were scattered around as well;
while little hills rose up on the sides of the route
and created innumerable arroyos that we had to
cross. The absence of inhabitants was evident and
could be an explanation, in part, for the abundant
vegetation, although it is possible that because of
our intrusion, any wayfarer would have preferred
to stay off the road, a healthy habit acquired during the long years of war. In order to cross some
sectors, it was necessary to utilize the four-wheel
drive transmission, especially to cross small
streams. Initially, we had calculated the duration
of the trip to be one hour (the major assured us it
would be between thirty and forty-five minutes). It
was not until two hours later that we entered the
town of Doa, having covered a distance of hardly 18
miles (30 kilometers). We were in Mutarara, in the
Tete province, which, according to the latest infor-

*mation from Human Rights Watch of 1994, was
the most heavily mined district in the country.*

*The images we saw were impressive, the general
rule being that destruction had not respected even
one building. From what we could surmise, Doa
had enjoyed a relatively high prosperity and importance before the war, judging from the number of
stores, public buildings, and houses constructed in
the typical Portuguese style. Without a doubt this
had given the town its color and beauty, which now
was only history. For several of the war years Doa
was in the hands of the government forces (FRE-
LIMO), in spite of the fact that the guerrillas (REN-
AMO) controlled the rural outskirts of the town.
Finally, after a bloody attack, the town succumbed
to the guerrillas in February 1992. This attack
would be the last and the largest battle of the war
in this region. The principal street, where we were
entering the town, had known better times, and
along its flanks were buildings and commercial
structures of one to three stories that, from their
arrangement, seemed to have been of some importance. Holes from mortars and other projectiles
were as evident on every side as the lack of doors,
windows, and roofs on the buildings that were still
standing, these having been taken by the people to
cover their own needs. Initially, it seemed to me
like a ghost town for the absence of people; but
when the news of our arrival began to spread, little by little the streets began to come to life.*

*The "posto de saúde" or health post was noth-
ing more than another destroyed house without
windows, doors, or roof. A sheet of metal that took
the place of a table and a portrait of Alfonso
Dakhalama, the president of RENAMO, hanging
on the wall—those were the only objects inside the
post. Médecins Sans Frontières had distributed
medication, which, according to our estimations,
would last only a few days more. Because of the
total lack of security at the health post, the said
precious, although basic, medications were kept in*

a box and were under the care of the military nurse. As for sanitation, the total lack of latrines was obvious, not only in the health post, but also in the rest of the town, as we would verify later.

Near the health post was the train station, which possibly had not seen the arrival of a single train in more than a decade. A few train cars, semi-destroyed and full of shell holes, were parked in the vicinity. In what had been the Doa-Chieza line, something caught my attention: a tree, several meters high, was growing exactly in the middle of the two rails of the track. The time it took for that tree to germinate and to grow must have coincided with the time that the station had ceased running trains.

Water was so scarce that it had become the day's most critical need. The little water that could be had, which does not satisfy the demands of the town of Doa, is obtained from little holes dug into the riverbed. However, we could see that not far away from here there had been a well with a hand pump that showed wear over time, but it obviously was not being used. Inquiring about that strange situation, one of the local authorities answered that before abandoning the place, the defeated FRE-LIMO soldiers had poisoned the well, and that at the other well they had broken the pump and thrown sacks of salt into its interior. It was of interest to learn the state of those wells in order to consider their possible rehabilitation, in case the damage wasn't major, and so we asked that they take us to the second well. It was not until later that we understood the looks that crossed the faces of the parade of people who were following us, their number curiously diminishing as we drew closer to the outskirts of the town. Here, the grass and thickets grew higher, and one noticed the absence of family gardens. The destruction of the ever more widely separated buildings was noticeable, confirming that we were nearing our destination. It was evident that none of the families that had returned from Malawi had settled in this area, in spite of the fact that the ground was apparently good for cultivation. We got out of the vehicle and set out to continue the journey on foot when I realized that the only ones left from the initial procession (besides us) were the RENAMO military. It seems Major Patrick understood my uneasiness and proceeded to explain to me that the area was the scene of the combat against the government forces, and that before the final assault of the guerrillas, the FRE-LIMO command had ordered the mining of the zone in order to stop the rebels' advance. I think that neither my companions nor I could have failed to be surprised, and of course it gave us some apprehension upon hearing the words, "the zone was mined." Immediately, the commandant explained that in the last few months a corridor had been demined, making it possible to get to the well, and that he would personally guarantee our safety if we would stay within the demined strip of land. We took him at his word, because he and his guerrillas were going on ahead of us across this tortuous route. Patrick explained to us that they had deactivated ninety-five mines in this area alone, the area where we were walking. What was outside of that was no man's land, since there still were many mines there.

After a few minutes of going along the sinister strip, we paused to look at what seemed to be some type of projectile. As confirmed by the major, it was a grenade that had never exploded. That exact site had seen the last and decisive battle, in February 1992, and the presence of the abundant number of bullets from Soviet AK47 assault weapons, mortar shots, and other war materials confirmed the story. It was even possible to identify the remains of what had been trenches and mortar positions.

Once at the well, we verified its deplorable state and because of the condition of the land around it and the access to it, immediate rehabilitation would be very difficult. A destroyed but lordly man-

sion stood close by as mute testimony to better times: we could still see the fine mosaics in the bathroom, the tub, and the chimney that were still in good condition, in spite of the want of roof, doors, and windows. The terrace of the mansion looked out over a large part of the region, but it was this strategic position that was also its ruin. The spectacle before our eyes was overwhelming. The defense of Doa took place around the country house, and during the fighting it was hit by several missiles that partially destroyed it. After that, time finally finished the job of destruction. It was impossible not to think about the former owners of such a beautiful house, about the lives they had led within those walls, about their hopes and dreams, and about their helplessness in having to abandon it—all because of war.

Leaving this dangerous zone, we continued on via a gravel road that took us to Chieza, a town that was gradually being populated by returning refugees. The fact that we were delving more and more deeply into rebel territory was no cause for relief within our group. We finally stopped at what once had been a camp for government troops and now under guerrilla control. It had become the principal rebel base in the district. This was enough to convince us that civilian and military control of the area was totally in the hands of the National Mozambican Resistance. Within the base, in the shade of a cabin, were a table and several chairs, where we supposed a dialogue would take place before our return. Wisely, the RENAMO command had chosen this place to exercise a certain amount of pressure in order that their demands be accepted. During the following hour, they made their requests, to which I responded in a manner that I thought quite adequate and diplomatic. Their petitions were as follows: medication and medical equipment, technical assistance to repair the wells or to construct new ones, and lastly, the construction of latrines. It was necessary to con-

vince them that the decision lay within the ARC office in Blantyre, since it would be ARC that would make the necessary medication and equipment available and give the authorization to begin the construction of the wells and latrines. Of course, my information would be key to their decision, and I promised that my report would be an honest reflection of what I had seen. Although I made no guarantees, I think that in the end my sincerity satisfied them.

Back in Doa and before undertaking the return to Malawi, Major Patrick extended an invitation to us that was difficult to refuse; he took us to his house. There, one could see the man of the house, the husband and father who cherished and cuddled his young children. The image of a guerrilla and authoritarian official fell away and it was almost impossible to think of Patrick as a member of a rebel group characterized as being among the most violent and bloodthirsty on the continent. Here, in his home, Patrick gave me a present: the mortar shell that we had found near the well, easily deactivated by the guerrillas. I was to keep this macabre gift until my departure from the refugee camps as a reminder of this journey. Chairs were quickly placed in front of the mud house, under the branches of a leafy mango tree, and within a few minutes we were presented with a drink that we felt obligated to accept: a palm wine or liquor. The drink we were offered was fresh, as the fermentation process had not yet begun. The flavor was exquisite, and I accepted another. A sensation of mental and physical lightness began to overtake me after finishing the second cup. The resonance of the ever-present drums turned into exaltation in that strange physical and mental state, perhaps produced by some chemical in the wine that is prepared following an old custom. Never did the African music and rhythm penetrate my body so intensely as it did that afternoon. Suddenly, I was not listening to the drums as if they were being

*played from the outside. Instead, I could feel the
beat deep within me, invading every cell of my body
and then breathing its way out to the exterior. I
imagine the people around me were experiencing a
similar effect for they started to dance, and it was
not too long before I joined them. I lost track of
time, and it was Noel, the driver, who reminded
me that we had to start our journey back to the
camp while there was still some light.*

*Noticing that the wine was to my liking,
Commandant Patrick gave me a five-liter plastic
container filled with the same wine, and after the
usual good-byes we began our return trip to
N'Gabu. It was quite a surprise when, only thirty
minutes later, the wine in the container began to
show clear signs of fermentation, and from then on
I had to take off the top every so often to let the
gases escape as they were accumulating rapidly.
After several days, back in Malawi, when the odor
from the flask was very strong, we decided to drink
it at a little get-together with some friends. The
pleasant flavor that I had remembered had been
replaced by another, very potent drink with a high
alcohol content. Major Patrick's gift became just a
memory along with the music and laughter of the
night, an occasion that we were seldom presented
with in N'Gabu.*

Later, ARC would use my report in meetings with
UNHCR and other international organizations to draw
their attention to this unprotected area. As a result, MSF
increased its number of helicopter visits to the area, and
UNHCR promised to accelerate the rebuilding of the
Tete-Chieza-Doa road as well as to continue with the
process of demining the area. ARC authorized me to
deliver a quantity of basic medication to the health post
at Doa. Difficult access, however, hindered ARC's promise to rehabilitate the health posts immediately.

I never had another opportunity to return to Doa nor
to see the major again. I only have memories left of the
area that made me feel the horrors of war, memories of a

people who—in spite of such grave inconveniences—continued to return to the land that was their home, a people who had hopes for a future in which their children would grow up and live in peace. I can still see the tree that had spread its roots, now buried in the midst of the train tracks, and I wonder what will happen when the day comes for the trains to return to the town. Perhaps the tree will be cut down to erase any memory of the brutal and violent epoch. Perhaps it will become a symbol; that future generations never forget the tragedy of the war. Or perhaps it will become an emblem of peace. I lean toward the last.

ANTIPERSONNEL LANDMINES: ANOTHER TRAGEDY IN MOZAMBIQUE

During the war years, both sides of the fight placed thousands of landmines, antipersonnel and antitank types, in broad areas of the country, frequently in flagrant violation of international laws, specifically the 1980 Conventional Weapons Convention Protocol II that prohibits and restricts the use of mines, booby traps, and other devices. Protocol requires that mines may only be directed at military objectives, and that "all feasible precautions be taken to protect civilians." There are two major weaknesses of the convention: First, it does not apply to internal armed conflicts where the most recent mine use has occurred; and two, there is no clear responsibility assigned for the removal of the mines. Despite the fact that both sides have denied it, RENAMO and FRELIMO placed mines in an indiscriminate and haphazard manner, and on occasion with the specific purpose of inflicting injury on the civilian population. Neither faction in the conflict made reliable maps in certain regions to correspond with the randomly placed mines.

Antipersonnel land mines infest the countryside, and the number may reach the chilling figure of 2 million, according to information from the United Nations. It has been established that the Portuguese placed mines in Mozambique during the colonial war; Rhodesia, South Africa, Tanzania and Zimbabwe placed others during the recent conflict. The land mines most commonly found in Mozambique are of Soviet origin: PMN (known as Black Widow), POMZ-2, and POMZ-2M, which correspond to the antipersonnel type.

RENAMO placed antitank mines in great number along the more important routes. Antipersonnel mines surrounded these landmines in order to avert, or at least to exacerbate the job of deactivating them. FRELIMO, on the other hand, used mines principally as a defensive mechanism against attacks on important structures or buildings. FRELIMO mined wide sectors, of the frontier with South Africa in the early years of the 80s, in anticipation of the possible invasion on the part of that country. Since RENAMO had several bases within Malawi from where it carried out attacks against FRELIMO military and civilian objectives, parts of the frontier with Malawi were also mined. These infernal artifacts have already claimed more than 10,000 victims since 1976, most of them civilian, and this number is growing with the process of repatriation, as the people return to work the fields and to penetrate areas that have been abandoned for years. More than 500 civilians have died or have been injured by mines since the war ended in October 1992. It is estimated that there have been more than 8,000 amputations in hospitals, although certainly this is an under-registered number since half of the injured died before arriving at the hospital and another five percent of the cases were not reported. Some of the government's isolated efforts to demarcate and to clear the mined zones have failed, because the impoverished population has stolen the wooden posts that marked the clearing, using them to cover their domestic needs or to sell them in the black market.

After fifteen years of civil war the economic impact is awesome: disabled bridges, hundreds of high-tension electrical towers destroyed, the infrastructure of health and education in ruins, the railroad—an essential part of commerce—inoperable in wide stretches, etc. The social impact is even greater, for there is no money that can return an amputated limb or lost vision. In 1989, the Asociacâo de Deficientes Mozambicanos (ADEMO)[1] was

133

founded; an organization that works broadly with Handicap International for the social and physical rehabilitation of individuals affected during the conflict. However, the journey is long, and the country must rediscover the road to peace; through production it must try to create jobs and to reintegrate into society those thousands mutilated and injured by war who will otherwise become a heavy burden upon their families and the state.

There are approximately 110 million mines in 64 countries around the world, and each year they kill or maim about 30,000 people. Mine stocks are estimated at 100 million. Five million new mines are laid each year; only 100,000 are cleared. The price of a land mine is US $3; uprooting one costs between $200 and $1,000. According to the International Committee of the Red Cross in Geneva, the only effective solution to the global crisis of land mines is their total prohibition and elimination, but strong opposition from countries such as China, USA, and Russia—which have stockpiled tens of millions of mines—makes it difficult to ban these devices. Meanwhile, mines continue killing or maiming thousands of civilians, usually those from poor countries; in what U.S. Democrat Senator Patrick Leahy calls "the worst of human depravity."

NOTES
1.   Asociacâo de Deficientes Mozambicanos (ADEMO) or Mozambican Disabled Association.

15

More Footsteps

Tete, Mozambique

The process of repatriation of Mozambican refugees from Malawi advanced to a quickened pace in the province of Tete, and many of the nongovernmental organizations expressed their desire to begin assistance and health projects in that Mozambican province. The American Refugee Committee was at the point of opening an office in Tete, the first in a series of steps to extend their activities in Mozambique. Meanwhile, an engineer from the U.S. who had worked with ARC earlier was designated as its representative in Tete, but it was considered important that a person from the health team in Malawi visit the province to meet with the local health authorities and to make on-location analyses in the areas that need health priority. That responsibility fell on my shoulders.

The constantly postponed trip to Tete, Mozambique, finally became a reality in September 1993. After a trip of approximately two-and-a-half hours from Mwanza, the majestic Zambezi River came into view for the first time. As soon as I crossed the bridge over this river, the city of Tete showed a facade similar to a port on the Pacific coast of South America. Up to a certain point, the city reminded me of the port of Guayaquil in Ecuador, although clearly of smaller size and less complexity than the "Pearl of the

Pacific." The history of Tete dates back to 1632, when the Portuguese established a military post on the Zambezi, one of the first European incursions into the interior of the African continent, on the site where the city rises today. The architecture is similar to the urban centers to which I had become accustomed before arriving in Malawi: houses and apartments spaced rather close together, buildings that did not go beyond ten stories, and an energy much more dynamic than anywhere else in Malawi.

For the next two days I held meetings with all the city and provincial health authorities and at the same time with representatives from several international organizations. It was a trial by fire for my Portuguese, since in official dealings they employ a rhetorical language filled with embellished phrases. It was exhausting work, not only for the number of meetings but also for the intense heat that bore down on the city. Temperatures of 113°F (45°C) are not a novel in this city whose name in one of the local dialects means "inferno." In the hot season the thermometer climbs beyond 122°F (50°C), and this is without considering the humidity factor, which is also elevated. After noon it is practically impossible to concentrate on one's daily labors unless one is in an air-conditioned office. Lethargy overtakes a great part of the population, which closes all commerce or suspends its activities, allowing itself to fall into a prolonged siesta from which it doesn't awake until long past 3:00 p.m. Activities reconvene until late into the night, taking advantage of the coolness of these hours.

The logistical difficulties identified during these few days would limit the effective performance of a health program. The district that the Provincial Health Department had assigned to ARC was connected to Tete by a third-class road that was open only during the dry season. During the winter months it was impassable, and therefore the programs we were to carry out in that area would be seriously affected for several months because of the lack of logistic and technical support necessary for subsistence. The presence of hundreds of antipersonnel and antitank mines in many of the roads of the province, especially in the districts of Mutarara and Moatize, was another latent problem that would affect the necessary intervention. By that time, there were many NGOs, bilateral and multilateral organizations trying to implement their programs in this part of the country. After the meeting with the provincial health director, I got the impression that his office was receiving a large number of applications from organizations eager to work in the province. I also noticed that they were beginning to loose track of all the agencies that came with their own set of proposals and priorities. One day, the director would appoint the Moatize district to ARC; the next day he would tell us that the International Rescue Committee was already carrying out health and sanitation activities in that area. It was clear that the lack of planning and the lack of a needs assessment were creating a chaotic situation in which several technical cooperation agencies were duplicating activities in a given area without proper coordination at the provincial level. It was going to take weeks of negotiation with the provincial health authorities to reach a final agreement that satisfied the two sides.

ZIMBABWE

At last, in September I was able to use my two weeks of vacation, taking advantage of a visit from John and Jeff Swartz, whom I consider my North American family. In December, my one-year contract would terminate, and I did not know what my destiny would be after that. One thing was clear: I wanted to stay in Africa.

One country, in particular, was attracting our attention for its variety of interesting places to visit: Zimbabwe. The country originally had been inhabited by hunters related to the bushmen who occupied areas of Namibia and Angola until the British South Africa Company took control of the region in 1890. In 1923, it became a British colony, taking the name of South Rhodesia. In 1965, the minority white government lead by Ian Smith ceded power and proclaimed Unilateral Declaration of Independence from Great Britain. Officially, Zimbabwe became independent on April 18, 1980, after a long civil war against the white government, and in the same year the African majority elected its first black president, Robert Mugabe. The Shona, the country's most important and most numerous ethnic group, comprises seventy-one percent of the population.

Harare, the city formerly known as Salisbury, is Zimbabwe's capital. Today, Harare is the largest urban center in Zimbabwe and offers all the services and comforts of modern life. Jacaranda trees, whose blossoms are of a beautiful violet color, abound in the innumerable open spaces and gardens of the city. We spent a day and a half touring Harare's commercial centers and pedestrian walkways. Zimbabwe is the only country where one can legally acquire pieces of sculptured ivory, and these are exhibited in many of the city's handcraft stores. A suitable policy for protection of the wildlife—conservation through utilization—has permitted the elephant population to grow. Under the Parks and Wildlife Act of 1975, wildlife was recognized as the property of those who lived with it, thus stressing local participation and utilization. Operation Windfall and the Communal Area Management Program for Indigenous Resources (CAMPFIRE) guarantee that benefits that result from the use of natural resources must remain in the local communities. This policy is working well in Zimbabwe, perhaps too well, for there is an over-abundance of certain animals such as the elephant. This fact has forced the culling of elephants to prevent over-population and extensive environmental damage. However, because of the ivory ban, in effect since 1989, Zimbabwe cannot sell elephant products overseas, and therefore cannot put this utilization policy into full effect. Nevertheless, it is important to recognize that since the ivory ban there has been a decline in poaching in countries without strong wildlife protection laws.

After Harare, we continued by air to the renowned Victoria Falls, located on the frontier between Zambia and Zimbabwe. On November 16, 1855, Dr. David Livingstone was the first white man to admire these impressive falls, and he baptized them in the name of his queen. Twice as high and almost double the width of Niagara Falls, in New York State, there are five different cascades that form this African marvel of nature: Devil's

Cataract, the Main Falls, Horseshoe Falls, Rainbow Falls, and the East Falls. Its width expands 5,400 feet or over one mile (1,700 meters), and its height extends from 190 to 315 feet (60 to 100 meters). We took in the Falls and its surroundings in two days. We made one interesting visit to "Spencer Creek," a ranch where we observed crocodiles in different stages of maturity. These reptiles are raised at the ranch, and later some fifty percent are returned to their natural habitat, while the other half is sacrificed for its precious skin, made into purses, shoes, or belts. In spite of the fact that this seems rather cruel, it is one way to protect an animal that otherwise would be totally exposed to the predatory nature of man.

The following adventure took on somewhat dramatic overtones, and my diary can tell the story:

September 1993

The route that descended to the base of the river was long, winding, and difficult. On one of our short rests, against the shattering noise of the rapids that could already be heard from that height, the instructor gave his first talk about safety. For the second time since we had embarked on this adventure, he again insinuated that it was not advisable for nervous persons or those with some cardiac problem to continue this undertaking. The common objective that united this group of eighteen people of different nationalities, ages, and sexes was daring: to run the rapids of the Zambezi River.

Minutes later we resumed the descent through a narrow corridor of wet and slippery rocks. At the second stop the talk instructed us on the correct use of the life jackets, advice about what to do if the boat overturned or if a person went adrift, that the important thing was to avoid panic, etc. At this point one middle-aged woman and her partner withdrew and took the offer of the return of ninety percent of the cost for cancellation. Then, right away we proceeded to sign a document in which we affirmed that we had been warned of the inherent risks in the crossing, and that we absolved the company from any responsibility in case of accident or death. One could feel the tension in the group at this moment, and I think that some people continued on only because of group pressure or because of not wanting to admit to the increasing fear they were feeling.

After some fifteen minutes more of descent, we finally arrived on a beach in the river's backwater, where there was a group of three rubber rafts of approximately 30x10 feet each (10x3 meters) and some kayaks that were easily maneuvered by the local guides who would accompany the group to provide better security. We divided into subgroups of six, each led by company guides, and we proceeded to put on our life jackets. Minutes later we got into the rafts and began the last stage of the lightning-flash training that we were to receive. Three of our group were placed in the front part and their mission was to prevent; with their combined weight, the nose of the raft to lift upon crashing into the waves. The three teammates in the back of the raft had a similar mission, although less critical. I opted to be in the front, and Jeff, my traveling companion, was placed in the back. The guide in charge of the oars took a seat in the middle of the raft and dictated precise orders as to when we could lean toward the nose of the raft so that, with our weight, we would avoid overturning this fragile vessel.

When our guide decided we were ready, we began the descent of the Zambezi River, whose current immediately began to grow in force and intensity, since the famous Victoria Falls were falling with an uncommon power at only some hundred meters upriver. The first rapids we crossed was grade 3 on a scale of difficulty of 6, which was a good start since it gave us a little more confidence and experience before facing the more difficult rapids. The adrenaline began to flow as the deaf-

ening noise of the water warned us that an even stronger rapids was ahead. The orders from the guide "Dive!" "Back!" arrived at the right moment, and we did not wait for a second command to carry them out. After successfully crossing one hair-raising grade 4 rapids, the river gave us a few moments of peace while we navigated through what seemed like a placid lake. We were able to spot hippopotamus skeletons on the shore. The guide explained to us that sometimes crocodiles and hippos get too close to the cataracts and fall. We were surprised to know that some animals survive this deadly fall. Some fishing eagles watched us from the sharp peaks that surrounded the river channel. This contemplative period didn't last long, for the familiar noise began to be heard again.

During the following hours we alternated the crossing of the rapids with spaces of tranquillity. Before the sixth of the important rapids the guide stopped the raft and warned us that the next one was grade 5 and the most difficult that we would cross, if we wanted to do it. Most of us, with the exception of one British girl, took the challenge, and we waited for a raft that would not cross the rapid, giving transit to the passenger who withdrew from the undertaking. I only remember that in front of me was a wall of water 30 feet (10 meters) high and the shout from the guide that ordered us to throw ourselves into the nose of the raft: "Dive!!" Truly, I don't know how we kept ourselves afloat in such a force of water. However, Jeff gave way to the harshness of one wave and fell into the water, although he never let go of the rope that went around the raft, and he was recovered as soon as we got to a calmer area. He came through it well although somewhat confused and without his precious glasses, left in tribute at the bottom of the mighty Zambezi.

After one pause for lunch and to recuperate our strength, there was even more excitement. For safety reasons no one crossed the most difficult rapid *(grade 6), and we went around it, carrying the rafts and walking on the shores. When we felt more confident for the success in crossing the rapids, we got to what would be the last of the trip, a rapid of grade 4.5. Perhaps overconfidence influenced us, so that we did not concentrate adequately, but a sideways crash of an eddy at the climax of the rapid twisted the raft, and all its occupants ended up in the water. I remember a few desperate seconds when I was underwater, and the terror at surfacing only to find myself under the overturned raft. Following the instructions for this and once over the initial panic, by using my hands I was able to propel myself toward the side of the raft until at last I was outside of it. Some friendly hands helped me to locate the lateral rope while the guide in the raft proceeded to count heads. Everyone was fine, and we extended our feet in front of us so we would not crash our heads against the many rocks in the area. After a few minutes that seemed like an eternity, we came to a backwater and were able to get the raft back into the correct position to restart the crossing.*

After some minutes, we came to the end of a most exciting adventure—drenched, exhausted but happy. The climb of some 2,500 feet (800 meters) to the top of the cliff was painful, not only for the length of the climb, but also because it was difficult to accomplish barefoot. When I fell into the water, my shoes were pulled off by the powerful current, and now they were resting at the bottom of the river. However, I consider it a just price to pay for having dared to disturb the restless dreams of the powerful Zambezi, one of the largest rivers of Africa.

16

MY LAST DAYS WITH THE ARC

October 1993

I had thought that it was a bad joke. A hyena in the storeroom! That simply could not be true. That Friday I was in Blantyre, the Malawi's most vital city, participating in a series of meetings with the American Refugee Committee health team, when I received the strange news from the watchman. Together with the other ARC functionaries, we went to the storehouse with a mixture of skepticism and curiosity. Curled up between boxes of supplies and the wooden crossbeams was an adult hyena, of a speckled species, trying in vain to shield himself from the eyes of the group of humans who had silently surrounded him. We could not understand how the hyena would be able to cross the whole city and get into our storeroom. Possibly at night? The animal was a yellowish-brown color with an abundance of gray spots, and it gave no indication of wanting to leave its newfound refuge. That gave us time to get a camera to photograph and document something that very few people would have been willing to believe. Little by little the hyena grew accustomed to our presence, which gave us a better opportunity to evaluate its condition. There were no evident signs of injury, but it seemed to have some problem with one of his back paws.

Back in the office, we began a search for some organization with the personnel and necessary resources to take charge of the situation. The first calls were to the police and fire departments, where skeptical officials, after their unfailing laughter, confessed their inability to take responsibility for the matter. The institution equivalent to an animal protection society lacked experience in cases of wild animals, but one employee was able to direct our search to the local zoo. After several attempts and much waiting on the line, I got through to someone at the zoo who had the experience and sufficient resources to put together some sort of strategy. After taking my name and the ARC address, he advised me to keep the curious away until he and his people arrived, which would be in less than an hour.

Thinking that the problem was practically resolved, we resumed our meeting. However, after only a few minutes, we were again interrupted by the sound of voices in the neighborhood of the storeroom, an annex to the offices. Instantly I heard a shot from a firearm, followed by an expectant silence. We immediately returned to the place of the original tumult, again without imagining the scene awaiting us. Lying in a puddle of blood was our fugitive, wild animal guest, expiring his last breath of life. Fortunately, his agony lasted only a short while, and when the last signs of life faded, we began to understand what had happened. An individual with the feared insignia of the MYP (Malawi Young Pioneers) was still pointing his gun at the immobile animal. His sardonic smile contrasted with the seriousness of the little group that witnessed the scene. In the few seconds of silence that followed, a feeling of hatred and helplessness awoke in me; I was confronted by one of the members of a group of fanatics, the Young Pioneers, who respected neither human life nor, least of all, that *of a poor animal. I noted something about the practices of this movement in earlier chapters, but I had never faced such cruel evidence in such a direct manner.*

This MYP official had been passing by and upon learning of the presence of the hyena, came in to our pantry, and before anyone could do anything, he discharged his gun toward the defenseless animal. After the initial shock, I began to recriminate him for his action and to point out that he had no right to enter ARC property without authorization, even less to fire a shot within its interior. Cleo, the accountant for the office, cautiously gave me to understand that I ought to end my accusations against a member of such a feared group, and he convinced me to leave.

I now think it was not necessarily the cruelty toward the hyena that infuriated me to such a degree; rather, it was the fact that this group continued to commit acts of this nature against innocent persons with total impunity. Some months later, an impassioned people, with the support of the army, assaulted the central seat of the Young Pioneers in Lilongwe, burned the building and destroyed other seats of MYP across the country. The arsenal of arms that was confiscated from this group was more sophisticated than that of the regular army, confirming the breath of the collaboration between this dark organization and the Mozambican guerrilla RENAMO. The end of one era of violence was coming nearer.

Back in the refugee camps, work returned to the routine trips, meetings, and program monitoring that was being implemented. As the days passed, the Chang'ambika camp was less occupied, and only during the distribution of food rations did the camp take on life, despite the fact that by the afternoon of the same day one could see a human column that, with its valuable cargo of food baskets, was crossing the invisible frontier line, returning to Mozambique. The majority of the population had two domiciles; one in some section of the refugee camp and the other in the Moatize district in Mozambique, on the other side of the frontier. This situation made it difficult to carry out our health programs inasmuch as it was very difficult to follow a floating population.

DISTRIBUTION OF FOOD RATIONS AND CORRUPTION

The office of the United Nations High Commissioner for Refugees in Malawi had tried on more than one occasion, although with little success, to take a census of the population in both camps. When the day of the census arrived, living quarters that were almost always unoccupied were transitorily occupied by their "owners." Somehow, news that there was going to be a census filtered out, and the people who had an interest in and benefited from the distribution of food rations heard of it. As described earlier, the refugees received a ticket once they were registered in a camp. That ticket gave them the right to receive food rations, which were distributed twice a month.

In Chang'ambika and Kunyinda, the administrators—civil employees of the government who were in charge of supervising the administrative activities of the camp—had the greatest interest in seeing that the number of refugees remained inflated, and that the number of rations was larger than the true number of people who had the precious ticket and who still resided in the camps. During food distribution, they sent their own people with a goodly number of tickets to receive extra rations which were then sold to intermediaries who roamed the place. What is certain is that the camp population tripled during the distribution days. By then, a wide sector of the population was already living beyond Chang'ambika. However, they received a double ration; one from the camp and one that was delivered to the Mozambican side. Moreover, the majority of the people already had a parcel of land that they were cultivating regularly. Therefore, the refugees sold the surplus at ludicrous prices to intermediaries who took advantage of the low prices to resell the products in cities throughout Malawi. The economic loss to UNHCR due to inadequate distribution of food reached millions of dollars, which came to mean the deterioration of other health programs.

Through the census, UNHCR, which was responsible for acquiring and transporting foodstuffs to the camps, hoped to determine the actual number of refugees and to suspend food rationing to those people who were not living in the camp permanently. In the area of healthcare, having reliable data about the camps was a very important aspect toward success, since it was necessary to know the number of vaccines to request, the maternal-infant population in the camp, or projections about the number of people at risk of suffering from cholera or dysentery among other ailments. Therefore, we had opted several months earlier to carry out our own census system. Every month the administrator of the camp was supposed to send a team to count the inhabitants of the different sections. Moreover, each month he would receive data listing births in deaths for each section, and with these figures he would present his demographic report to UNHCR and to us. According to an agreement with the Ministry of Health in January 1993, the health surveillance assistants (HSA) would go out every month to make house visits, aside from monitoring the state of hygiene, to verify the existence of latrines, to review the vaccination cards, and to count the number of people in each domicile. Using this more subtle form enabled us to obtain more exact demographic data without inconveniencing the population or provoking suspicion among them. Prior to this new practice, UNHCR census takers had been pulled away and stoned when they tried to take a surprise census.

As an example of the discrepancy, data from the Office of the Presidential Cabinet (OPC), which was supplied by the administrator of the camp, listed 26,710 refugees in Chang'ambika and 64,212 in Kunyinda during the month of April 1993. Our figures for the same month were 21,617 and 42,103 refugees, respectively, in the same camps. That makes a difference of 5,000 refugees in Chang'ambika and 22,109 in Kunyinda, which the civilian authorities could not explain.

Another achievement that came from the agreement with the Ministry of Health was the right of the ARC staff, including our health assistants, to accompany the health teams. With this we were assured of even more accuracy in the data. During one meeting with the UNHCR people, we presented our data, and, from then on, they began to use our statistics to get a better idea of the population in the camps. Later, UNHCR proposed the possibility of using the HSA monthly visits to take a surprise census; one that ARC would supervise. This responsibility, which fell on me, was somewhat compromising since, if the true nature of this activity (which was considered routine) were discovered, we would lose credibility with the population, and several of the community programs we maintained would come to ruin. Of course, there was some internal and external pressure since UNHCR authorized and financed several of our programs in Malawi and in Mozambique. So, in order to obtain results, I found myself involved in an operation that would have to be replicated in other parts of the country.

In order to prevent information from leaking out, we maintained the utmost caution from the very beginning. A nucleus of only five administrators (the health coordinator and the field officer for UNHCR in Malawi, the ARC director, the health advisor and myself) knew the date and the details of the operation that would take place primarily in Chang'ambika and Kunyinda. The designated day arrived, and the HSA teams, together with our people, were ready to begin the job, when an "observer" joined each of the teams. These observers were nothing less than delegates from UNHCR who were charged with noting the identification numbers of the abandoned housing and the names of their owners in order to withdraw their duplicate cards later or simply to cancel them at the next distribution of food. At this point, the HSA team received the final details, and we began the day's activity. During the morning, we determined that one-half the housing was unoccupied, which we marked and annotated. It seemed that by the afternoon, the people began to suspect our intentions and a small flow of humanity began to cross the frontier. In any case, the day's work was finished, and the information came much closer to reality. In Kunyinda, a similar procedure took place. During the next distribution of rations, we took cards away from the unscrupulous people who had acquired two or three of them, or from those who no longer resided in the camp. With this operation, we accelerated an irreversible but necessary process, that of repatriation.

SUSPENSION OF FOOD DISTRIBUTION IN CHANG'AMBIKA

Although corruption in food rationing continued through the course of the following months, our operation ostensibly reduced the number of phantom cards. However, during September it was evident that Chang'ambika population continued to decline, a fact that was reflected in the number of consultations and admissions to our health units. The Respiratory Care Unit and the dysentery room were closed. The Intensive Nutrition Center held only 25 children, as compared to the 100 there last January. The Cholera Unit registered practically no incoming patients.

At the same time, a conflict arose; with the Malawi government and UNHCR-Malawi on one side, urging the departure of the Mozambican refugees from Malawi territory, and UNHCR and the Mozambican government on the other side, both of them trying to postpone the repatriation process, arguing that the basic conditions in that country were still precarious. Under some pressure it was agreed to stop food distribution in the Mulanje district camps immediately and to continue with food distribution in Chang'ambika only until December 1993. To stop food distribution was the equivalent of closing the camp, a necessary step to accelerate passive or voluntary repatriation back to Mozambique. The official act of closing the camp would follow soon after, and UNHCR would begin the costly and difficult operation of transporting the remaining refugees back to their own country—a process called active repatriation, for it requires the use of hundreds of trucks and buses.

For the ARC personnel, the work decreased in intensity, and the last weeks of my contract, which culminated at the beginning of December, were dedicated to training the Mozambican health personnel who were getting ready to return to their own country. One of the achievements of those last weeks was obtaining recognition from the Malawi and Mozambique health authorities for several training courses we had awarded with certificates during the year. These officially recognized certificates, delivered in a meaningful ceremony, would therefore be legally recognized in Mozambique, which increased the possibility of work for our dear APEs.[1]

AN EMOTIONAL GOODBYE

It was with great apprehension that I awaited the last day of my duties as district health coordinator for ARC. In Kunyinda, the day arrived one week earlier, when I made my last supervisory visit and took the opportunity to say goodbye to the ARC personnel in that camp. It was moving to hear one and then the next ask that I renew my contract, but there was not much left to do on that side of the frontier. Alfred Mahoney, the health advisor at Kunyinda, also came to ask me to take him as an aide in case I contracted with another health organization in Malawi or Mozambique.

Chang'ambika was my true home, and I knew that saying goodbye to my associates and friends there would be even harder. On the last day of work, the first day of December 1993, I arrived punctually at the camp and noticed a strange atmosphere. I made my rounds of daily visits to the health units and to the few patients who were still in admittance, but on the way to the Intensive Nutrition Center I had the impression that in some way my progress was being held up by a series of interruptions, most of them trivial. When I arrived at last, a group of almost 200 people were crammed into the nutrition center to greet me: personnel from the health center, the whole ARC health team and the ARC workers, the camp's civilian authorities, representative chiefs from the different ethnic groups, mothers of children from the nutrition center, school teachers, soccer players, and friends in general had come together in this tiny space. The whole place was covered with messages written in three different languages—English, Portuguese, and Chichewa—that

wished me a safe return to my *kuniumba*, my mother-
land. There were so many phrases written that it was
impossible for me to read all of them at that moment,
except for some of the larger ones, and they were enough
to bring tears to my eyes. They had also improvised a
small table with a cake, flowers, and simple adornments.

Once past the initial surprise, a series of short
speeches began sincere phrases in which they thanked
me for my work during those intense twelve months.
Many participated, but there were also those who wanted
to say some spontaneous words to me, such as the mother
who, in the Yao language, thanked me for having saved
her child from possible death from cholera and acute malnutrition. She began a song—my favorite—and all the
women present joined in a chorus. Others took their turn
to speak: the camp administrator, the director of the
health center, the director of the school, the captain of
the soccer team, the leaders of the music and dance
groups, the efficient Stanley Banda, Lou Cooney and Chief
Chang'ambika. At the end of a long list of speeches it was
my turn, and with much difficulty, for emotion had overcome me, I recounted my arrival in the camp, my aspira-
tions, my satisfactions and disappointments, and
expressed my eternal gratitude to those kind people who
had given me a lesson in life and who were responsible for
the difficult but nevertheless significant transformation
that took place deep within me. I asked them to remember the naive Ecuadorian doctor who came a year ago with
the belief that hard work and commitment were enough
to solve most of their health problems. I asked them to see
the man they were facing now, to perceive the changes
that had occurred in such a short time among them. Yes,
they could sense the difference, and I could feel their
acceptance, for now their lives were linked with mine; it
did not matter how far I would be from there, for in my
heart had become black, and Africa will live in me forever. I could not continue on, for my tears got in the way.

Following the tradition of offering gifts to those
departing, I received several presents, among them
African crafts, and a soccer shirt with the number 9 (for
the position that I played), the name of the camp, and my

last name on it. Perhaps the most significant gift came at the end when they gave me a sum of money, together with some papers in an envelope. The paper listed more than 300 refugee names and the amount in *kwachas*[2] that each one had voluntarily contributed. It was such a moving gesture that I did not have the words to thank them; I knew that I must accept it because to do otherwise would have offended them, but at the same time it hurt me to accept money from people who had such difficulty in obtaining it. Centavo by centavo they had collected the money that not only had an incalculable sentimental value, for it represented the spontaneous recognition of hard labor, but also was understood to represent a positive response from the community.

At the end, an old man whom I did not remember came to the front and in a slow Chichewa thanked me for "the goodness that you brought to the camp, for the sick that you cured, for the young for whom you helped to set their sights higher, and for not having behaved like other whites." Taking a step toward me, he gave me a wrapper of newspaper. "I know the return to your *kuniumba* [home] is long," he said to me. "The only thing that I could get was this little bit of sugar and pasta to help you make the long return journey. However, I hope that Africa will see more of you."

Leaving Chang'ambika, an emptiness began to come across me. The children said goodbye to me in their own way, with the salute they always made me, running behind the car and shouting, "*Mzungu* [white ghost], Benjamin! Benjamin!" Left behind were the familiar faces of those whose lives had filled mine for a year. Truly, African people with whom I had shared pain and joy, dreams and illusions, people whom I had come to consider my friends. The words of the old man went round and round in my mind and the word "Africa" took on dimensions unknown until then. Something told me that I still could not leave this magic continent with which I was definitely in love.

NOTES

1. *Agente Polivalente de Enfermedades,* or Disease Prevention Worker. In Mozambique this is the equivalent to "community health worker."
2. *Kwacha* is the official currency of Malawi. In 1993, 4 kwachas were equivalent to US$1 dollar.

PART THREE

17

A New Step in Africa

Weeks of Decisions

A few days before I finished my duties with the American Refugee Committee, I received a formal proposal to assume the position as resident physician for an Italian company at the base camp of a dam-building project on the Shire River. After a meeting with the manager of the project, they made an offer to me, and I asked for a few days before giving an answer. The dispensary that would be under my supervision had all the physical means and the health personnel necessary to function well. The possibility of staying in Africa, a rather attractive salary for Latin American standards, and the proximity of the site to Blantyre seduced me into accepting the post despite the fact that it meant I would spend the second consecutive Christmas away from my family. The workplace was in the Mwanza District, some 45 miles (70 kilometers) from Blantyre, close to the town of Tedzani on the banks of the Shire.

South Africa and Apartheid

Before beginning my work, I took advantage of the six-day interval to travel to a country that for many reasons had attracted me a great deal, South Africa. At that time, it was in its last stage of apartheid. This short trip included a stay in Johannesburg and a visit to friends, a Belgian couple, the Damans. This big city began as a mining town, when the largest gold deposits in the world were discovered in 1886 in Witwatersrand. Johannesburg, the "city of gold," is the largest commercial center in South Africa, with its population of two million inhabitants. The white neighborhood where the Damans lived is a prototype of an elegant neighborhood in any part of Western Europe or the United States, with every kind of commodity available. However, there is an impressive security system that includes walls, barbed wire fences, private guards, closed circuit television, and alarms of every sort. For many years, the white population has lived in these islands of luxury and comfort, while not too far away, Africans barely managed to survive in the infamous townships.

The system of apartheid—the Afrikaans word for "apartness"—began with the election of the white National Party in the late 40s and with the passage of the Prohibition of Mixed Marriages Act in 1949. In the 60s, the white government decided that blacks could not own property, and they expropriated houses, stores, and lots, expelling black homeowners from places like Alexandra, a black area north of Johannesburg, surrounded by affluent white suburbs. World opinion turned against this system after a series of events, including the 1960 Sharpeville Massacre, where the police killed sixty-seven blacks, and the 1962 arrest of a man who would become part of world history: Nelson Mandela. In 1968, the International Olympics Committee barred South Africa's team from the games; in 1977, the United Nations imposed an arms embargo on the country; and in 1986, the U.S. Congress voted for economic sanctions. The economy of South Africa slipped into a long recession. By this time black illiteracy reached fifty percent, and unemployment stood at forty-six percent nationally.

On the weekend after my arrival, Jack and Vivian Daman took me to the independent territory of Bophutatswana in the southeast of the Transvaal. There one finds what is known world-wide as Sun City, a vacation complex of first-class hotels, of which the most famous is Lost City, of such luxury and splendor that it is difficult to describe. In its outskirts there is a wild life park, where guests may make a private safari by day; at night they can attend the many first-class shows that the hotel presents daily, or they can try their luck in the casino. Instead of continuing to describe this place, it seems more important to analyze the extreme differences between the black majority and the white minority who barely reach fifteen percent of the total population. Traveling for three hours along the route from Johannesburg, it was possible to see towns where blacks were living in an obvious state of complete abandonment and poverty. Eight million live not in houses, but in the squalor of squatter shacks. Approximately 18 million black families each earn less than $220 a month. The violence in Natal, Soweto, or in Johannesburg has received world coverage and the policy of racial segregation has brought criticism and economic sanctions that have isolated the country for several decades.

In the last years of apartheid, however, the South Africa's president, Frederik Willem de Klerk, instituted a series of changes to improve the situation for blacks, and for the first time opened up the possibility of presidential elections in which the African majority could exercise the right to vote, until then an exclusive right of the white minority. At the end of 1993, there were still beaches reserved exclusively for whites and certain zones or residential neighborhoods that prohibited blacks. Schools were segregated, and the quality of education in black schools—Bantu education—was far inferior to that provided in white schools. High- and middle-level managerial posts were the privilege of the whites, while work considered degrading was relegated to people of color, who as described earlier, could neither own property nor choose the place where they wanted to live. The white government was beginning to ease its harsh policies against non-whites, hoping perhaps to gain support for the next elections.

The social and political changes occurring in South Africa received worldwide attention because of their strong influence over other countries in the region, having economic, political and military interests there. South Africa has vast amounts of natural resources; it is the world's leading producer of gold and other valuable metals. For the last few years, the National Party has financed civil wars and revolutions in countries such as the former Rhodesia (today Zimbabwe), Mozambique, Namibia, and Angola. Africa's black regimes had repudiated South Africa's white government, forbidding entry visas for South African citizens. The only exception, as noted earlier, was Malawi, a nation that had benefited from its openness with South Africa, receiving in exchange, technical and financial assistance over the course of several years. For decades and as a product of the policy of racial segregation, the Republic of South Africa lived in isolation from the rest of the world. Its citizens were restricted from obtaining visas for many countries, an important commercial embargo affected the mercantile relations of South Africa with the rest of the world, and cultural interchange was practically nonexistent, this including sports figures who could not compete in any major international event. International pressure took its toll, and the white government found itself obliged to call for multiracial presidential elections.

One night, the Damans invited a white South African couple to dinner at their house, and for some agreeable time the conversation covered many different topics. After dinner, the inevitable theme of the coming multiracial elections arose, and the lady clearly let it be known that her position was shared by many whites who feared their privileges would diminish if the power of the government fell to the black majority. What drew my attention the most was this couple's obvious sympathy with the extreme rightist party—Afrikaner Resistance Movement—that was opposing the free elections in the country. Its neo-fascist leader Eugene Terre'Blanche vowed to fight if the black majority seized power. Using disrespectful terms, the Damans' guests asserted that the only solution for bringing the racial problem to an end was "to wipe those monkeys from the face of the earth." Without wanting to offend my hosts, I opted to change the theme of the conversation radically, which fortunately took effect and the rest of the evening transpired without incident.

In summary, my first visit to South Africa served to destroy a number of myths that I had held about the country and its white supremacist government. During a second visit to this country, specifically to Cape Town, I witnessed the excitement and violence that preceded the presidential elections of May 1994. However, as there are people with radical ideas, there are others who are committed to achieving social change. I believe that the majority of South Africans do not want to see their country immersed in a bloody civil war of unforeseen consequences. I prefer to believe that the majority favor a nation that provides equal opportunities to all its citizens, whatever their race might be.

A DOCTOR IN A WORK CAMP

After returning to Malawi at the end of this short vacation, I arrived with my few belongings in Tedzani, the base work camp for the Lower Shire dam. My new employer seemed to have forgotten my arrival since the efficiency apartment they offered me was not ready, and for the first three days I was put up in the house of one of the directors of the project who had recently left. From this moment on, I noticed certain aspects that, in spite of seeming insignificant at the time, in the near future would take another, more grave, turn. However, I immediately began my work as medical officer for the camp.

The dispensary consisted of two rooms for outpatient consultations—one of those had two beds for observation—a waiting room, a pharmacy, and a bathroom. One Toyota truck had been outfitted to function as an ambulance. As for the personnel, there were three nurses, one nurse's aide, and two ambulance drivers. The dispensary held an excellent stock of medication and medical materials, a steam-pressure sterilizer and an ultraviolet light sterilizer, an examination table, a refrigerator, a glucometer, a hemostat, and a light microscope, among other useful items. With this equipment and personnel, I was to look for the health care and supposedly the occupational safety of almost 3,000 African workers and 60 Italian and South African expatriates and their families.

The efficiency apartment assigned to me consisted of a study, a rather large bedroom, and the bathroom. The three daily meals were prepared and served in the club that, besides the restaurant services, had a community room with a television with a dish antenna and some table games (for example billiards and darts). There was a swimming pool located a few meters from the club, and during the first weeks, that gave me my only opportunity for exercise. Later on, it was closed for maintenance for an indefinite period. I could not believe the difference with my previous living conditions, where I lacked all the basic comforts. Nevertheless, I missed my little house in N'Gona and the company of my African neighbors.

In the first weeks, I divided my time between seeing outpatients and reorganizing the dispensary. I made an inventory of the pharmaceutical supplies as well as the rest of the materials and equipment, changed the work shifts of the medical personnel and support staff without cutting into their rest hours, so that there would be an attendant on duty twenty-four hours a day, and improved the system of statistics and epidemiological surveillance. Company policy dictated that I personally examine the expatriates, while the nurse attends the Africans unless the case merited my intervention. The second week after my arrival, a new project supervisor from Italy arrived and in a few days he called me to his office to introduce myself. The project was suffering from setbacks, and a few weeks before the beginning of my contract an earth-slide in one of the tunnels cost the life of two Africans and gravely injured five others. With these antecedents, the company administration had decided to send this new supervisor who was known for his authoritarian style, which he soon put into place in Tedzani. Thus began a series of dismissals and changes across the camp; week-end leaves were almost completely suspended and a cli-mate of tension began to permeate the atmosphere. These Draconian methods affected every department and division. A short time later I received the first memorandum from the supervisor in which he referred to the "audacity and abuse" of the nurses in using the ambulance during the nights "without authorization," when the truth was that at the end of a night shift, this means of transport took them to their homes in the black quarters of the camp. Upon trying to explain the reason for the use, he simply replied to me that "black personnel may not use the ambulance, under no circumstances."

Until these steps were taken, I was accustomed to visiting my friends from the MSF mission in Mwanza for a few hours on Sundays. I had maintained excellent relations with them since my days with ARC. Guillermo Bertoletti, the mission head, and the group of French nurses never failed to be the perfect hosts. Upon the restriction of weekend leaves, the camp began to seem more like a prison, and had it not been for the sporadic visits of one of the MSF nurses, Sabine Hugo, a descendent of the great writer Victor Hugo, the confinement would have been insufferable. I met Sabine while I worked with ARC and was immediately impressed with her thoughtfulness towards the refugees. She loved African children, and more than once I found her carrying a baby on her arms or feeding malnourished children herself while she spoke to them in a broken Chichewa with a heavy French accent. She had previously worked with MSF in the Sudan and had the knowledge, the experience, and the willingness to volunteer for a second tour in Africa. Initially, it was difficult to imagine Sabine working with such an outspoken character as Guillermo, who, as a health coordinator and as a friend, learned to like and respect this unpretentious and hard working woman.

At this point I should describe the camp a bit. On a hilly side of the camp rose the residential sector, where there were brick constructions with all the basic services, and these were for the foreign technicians. There were houses for those who were there with their families, efficiency apartments like mine for the professional personnel, and single rooms for expatriate workers (most of them coming from Italy and South Africa). At the other end of the base was the "black quarter," where laborers and miners as well as African professional personnel cohabited. The poor housing lacked electricity and drinking water; the overcrowding and the hygienic conditions were stifling. No blacks could visit the white part unless they did domestic work for the expatriates. They had been successful in obtaining dining service for the African professionals, i.e. engineers, architects, and administrators. However, their dining hours were distinct from those of the whites, and if they arrived late they lost their opportunity to eat.

January 1994

This morning the number of patients in the dispensary was more than usual. The waiting room was jammed with workers who, for the most part, were suffering from malaria or from work-related injuries. The excessive number of work hours that has been the rule for several weeks has had a negative influence, since fatigue has made the workers more susceptible to making mistakes at dangerous jobs or while operating dangerous machines. This was reflected by a growing number of cases of eye injuries, falls, and amputations, which we treated in the dispensary or referred to the regional hospital.

The lunch schedule for whites is from 12:00 noon to 1:00 p.m.; for black professionals it begins at 1:00. For the amount of work on this day, I was not able to eat at my appointed hour, and I got ready to eat at the second shift. By now I can count several friends among the African personnel, and after filling my tray with an assortment of dishes that were on the menu today, I invited Trevor, an African engineer, and another black professional to sit with me for lunch. They hesitated for a moment but ended up by accepting my invitation. I had not noted that there were two or three whites at a table in the back from the first shift. As soon as my two Malawian friends had seated themselves, one of those Italian miners made use of his powerful voice to demand that "the blacks leave that table." Explaining to them that I had personally invited them, the miner informed me that it was a white table, and that they could not stay there. Without saying a single word, Trevor and his friend took their trays and withdrew in spite of my protestations to ignore the affront. The incident left me upset and confused, but I recovered in a few seconds and, taking my tray, I went to the table my friends had chosen. Directing my voice to the table of the expatriates, I asked if there were some law that kept me from sitting at a black table and without waiting for their reply I proceeded to sit down. Episodes like this are repeated daily in the camp which, little by little, is being converted into an intolerable place.

When at last the new ambulance arrived, something I had counted on as necessary equipment, the project supervisor delineated through a memorandum the uses for this piece of transportation, limiting it almost exclusively to service for the white personnel. A truck would be made available two times a week to transport the black patients, if the case required transfer to the hospital in Blantyre. In the face of this insult to human rights, I sent the first of a series of memos in which I rejected these inhumane measures, but the decision was not modified. By the second month, the situation was becoming untenable for the continued interference by the supervisor. Expatriates and operators alike arrived at the consulting room, suffering from no ailment but at the point of exhaustion from working forty-eight hours straight, longing for a few minutes of peace before returning to their work. The cases of hyperthermia[1] among the miners who were working on the construction of the tunnel rose day by day; temperatures inside the tunnel could be verified as 122°F (50°C). Malaria scourged the camp, and there was not a day that twenty to thirty cases were not attended. Sexually transmitted diseases, including AIDS, rose to epidemic proportions, also affecting the white population.

165

The many memos and letters I sent to the supervisor included suggestions and recommendations to decrease the incidence of certain diseases and to improve the occupational safety of the African workers. I never received a response. On the other hand, the administration immediately reacted to my report on the increase of sexually transmitted diseases among expatriates, although in a way I did not intend. In a private meeting, I was asked to prepare a list with the names of these people, a request I refused to comply with, for it went against medical ethics. I found out later that a "black list" was used as an excuse to dismiss people.

The episode that was to try my patience to the limit came a few weeks later when we received a Malawian patient with three metal splinters encrusted in the cornea of his right eye. For several weeks, I had been insisting on the necessity of providing protector glasses for the workers who cut metal. No answer or action came from the administration, and we continued receiving patients with ocular or facial injuries caused by metal splinters. This patient presented a particularly serious picture for the metal splinters were deep within the cornea, and in the dispensary we could do nothing more than arrange for his transfer to the Queen Elizabeth Hospital in Blantyre. The ordeal for this poor fellow began with the consequent wait for the company truck that would take him to Blantyre. According to the established rule, the truck could be used for this purpose only two days a week, so that the patient had to return the following morning. However, that day the truck was consigned for other work, which was confirmed too late to take some other action. By the afternoon of the third day there was still no transport authorized for this patient, and I made a unilateral decision to send him in the ambulance, which use was restricted to whites. At the hospital, the ophthalmologist could not see him until the following day when it was already too late, for the specialist could only confirm that the eye was blinded.

Writing to the British colleague, who attended this man, I asked for information about the case and whether or not early intervention would have saved the eye. The answer was categorical: specialized attention within the first forty-eight hours after the injury could have saved the patient's eye. The same day that I received this information, I drew up my resignation, attaching one copy of the same medical information and the three memos in which I urged the facilitation of transportation for the patient. At the same time, I wrote a letter of protest to the Medical Council of Malawi in order to document such an egregious deed. In this last letter, I mentioned that in the last six months there already had been three doctors who had left the same company for similar reasons. Fifteen days later I left the camp with a mixture of joy and pain. Relieved for leaving behind a place where the African is mistreated daily, where flagrant violations of human rights are committed. Pained for leaving the hard working health personnel without the support that I could give for this short stay. The personnel director was at the simple farewell to present his thanks in the name of the Africans.

As a sad epilogue to this experience, three months passed, and still they had not finished paying me my whole salary; meanwhile the company was facing a series of labor trials. The massive dismissals, the work-related accidents, and the failure to make payments were the order of the day. Without a doubt, this short stay in Tedzani would become the most disagreeable experience in all my stay in Africa.

NOTES

1. Hyperthermia is an elevation in body temperature.

18

THE PRINCIPAL OBJECTIVE: TO STAY IN AFRICA

NEW ALTERNATIVES

During the week following my departure from the Italian company, I rested at my friend, Bashir Sacranie's house in Blantyre and began searching for work that would allow me to stay in Africa a little longer. Actually, the idea of leaving the continent never entered my mind. For some reason, I felt that my mission in Africa was not complete, and that I needed more time to gain experience.

Mozambique refugees in Malawi continued returning to their devastated country, and a new and final phase was about to begin with their return. The health programs constituted one vital component for the success of the repatriation plan that was the last step in a sequence of events begun some years earlier with the arrival of the refugees and the consequent emergency, the establishment and consolidation of health programs for this disenfranchised population, and, finally, the refugees' difficult return to their homeland.

When the Italian company finally paid me what they owed, they partially paid it in the form of an air voucher that could not be exchanged for cash. The travel agent, Mr. Noah, offered me several alternatives, among them a trip to India, taking advantage of an excellent discount on the airfare. So, in February 1994, while awaiting confirmation about some job offers, I fulfilled a dream of visiting this exotic and legendary land.

I was taken by the beauty of India. The contrasts between the rich and the poor are extreme; one could marvel at the Taj Mahal's majesty, and moments later, one could cry at the misery of the children digging for food in piles of rubbish. I tried to avoid the places advertised in the tourist packages (except Agra and the Taj Mahal), and ended up visiting Jaisalmer, Amber, and the Thor Desert, where searching for adventure, I hired a man and his camel for a two-day journey on the hot dunes near the border with Pakistan. Again, during the stay in India, my skin color created confusion and people talked to me in Hindi or in Punjabi, thinking that I came from the Northern state of Punjab, where people are "taller and whiter".

For several weeks after returning to Malawi, I stayed with Conny Arvis, a diplomatic officer with the U.S. Embassy in Lilongwe. Her home became the center of operations in my job search, which was to have a positive result in the following days. Some time earlier, Médecins Sans Frontières of France and its program in Malawi had contacted me about an opening in their program in Mozambique, specifically for the position as health director of the MSF mission in Zambezia province. Because there was a two-year minimum time requirement, I declined the offer for the position, which was later filled by a French doctor. In March, MSF informed me that there was another position, this one of shorter duration, in the Milanje district in Mozambique. After expressing interest in that position, I sent my application to MSF-Mozambique for consideration. Whatever the answer, it would not come until after Easter.

During the interim, Conny and I made plans to take a trip somewhere within the African continent. We considered Kenya, Tanzania, Madagascar, Namibia, and South Africa. The last two countries prevailed; Namibia for the mystery surrounding it, and South Africa for the possibility of getting to know Cape Town better.

Namibia

The beginning of the trip was somewhat difficult. In Johannesburg, it was not even possible for us to leave the airport because of the violence preceding the presidential elections, which had claimed dozens of victims in the last few days. My entry visa to Namibia was finally arranged through the offices of Air Namibia in the Jan Smuts International Airport, and I received it via fax only minutes before our flight departed. A few days later, white rightists detonated car bombs in downtown Johannesburg and at the international airport, killing 21 people and injuring more than 150. After that contretemps we finally landed in the capital of the new Republic of Namibia, Windhoek, a city about which we had little information prior to the trip. The influence of South Africa, the country to which Namibia belonged until only five years earlier, was evident from the airport. Signs in Afrikaans, German, and English evinced the predominant currents of the country. The South African rand was still the official currency, despite the fact that the government was introducing a new national currency, the Namibian dollar.

As for early history, little is known about this region before 400 years ago, when the Portuguese landed on its coasts. The first whites to visit the interior were missionaries, hunters, and traders. In 1884, Germany took possession of what was then known as German Southeast Africa. In 1915, during the First World War, South Africa took control of this territory. In 1920, the League of Nations awarded a mandate to the Republic of South Africa for the region, but the United Nations abolished that mandate in 1966. During the 60s, SWAPO, the military branch of a Marxist movement, began a guerrilla war against South Africa's occupation forces, a conflict that mounted in intensity in 1975, when Portugal withdrew from Angola and Cuban forces landed in the country in support of the Marxist government of MPLA, which was allied with SWAPO. Namibia finally achieved its independence from South Africa on March 21, 1990, and elected a black president, Sam Nujoma, who had moderate Marxist tendencies, but heads a democratically run country to this day.

Namibia is one of the world's least densely populated countries, with an average of barely 2 inhabitants per square kilometer. It has a population of 1.6 million; 86 percent are black, 7 percent white, and 7 percent mulatto. The Ovambo are the principal ethnic group of the country, representing 50 percent of the population, followed by the Kavango, 9 percent; the Herero, 8 percent; and the Damara, also at 8 percent.

Namibia and Botswana are the only countries where one can still find the Bushmen, specifically in the Kalahari. The Bushmen, a group of people who used to inhabit the entire southern area of the continent, are a nomadic people for whom the concept of owning land is unknown, and they rarely stay in one place for very long. For their short stature they can be considered almost pygmoid given that their height, on average, barely reaches 4 feet, 9 inches (150 centimeters). The white man's excessive big game hunting has contributed to the group's decimation. Their language, known to the white man as "the click language," is truly difficult to describe, for it is characterized by peculiar sounds that are accompanied by frequent clicks.

A Nissan Sentra was waiting for us at the airport, its rental arranged from Malawi. After a night's rest in Windhoek, a city of 120,000 inhabitants, we began a journey that would cover a part of the country's 318,260 square miles (824,296 square kilometers). Okahandja, the land of the ferocious Hereros, was the first stop, followed by Outjo. During the next day, we continued in a northerly direction, crossing the Damaraland. There we visited the town of Khorixas, a petrified forest 200 million years old, and the thousand-year-old petroglyphs of Twyfelfontein— all in breathtaking desert landscape. Traveling westward, we reached the renowned Skeleton Coast, so named for the number of shipwrecks and whale skeletons that guard this treacherous Atlantic coast. When we arrived at the beach, a dense fog was covering the area, adding a touch of mystery, which was accentuated even more by the fresh tracks of some wild animal marauding the coast. Our first thoughts were of a lion, but later we confirmed that it was a hyena, which hunts seals and other marine mammals. The desert landscape, so clouded, put a dramatic touch on the day's trip, as was the absence of any human footstep for miles around. The desert, which is never the same, manifests itself in different manners and forms with the variety of arid regions. The gamut of colors in this dry zone runs from sandy gray to intense yellow and includes a reddish tone that we saw on our route to the region of Burn Mountain.

After reaching the Atlantic Ocean, we began our trip southward, traveling along the coast. We passed Cape Cross, the site where the Portuguese arrived in the fifteenth century; then Henties Bay and later Swakopmund, a beautiful city of some 7,000 inhabitants, where one senses the German influence in the facades. In the morning, after a breakfast of Schwarzwalderkirschtorte (Black Forest Cake), we continued on to the port of Walvis Bay, which was returned to Namibian control only days earlier, after having been under South African rule until 1994. We went on to the Namib-Naukluft Desert, one of the most spectacular desert ecosystems in the world, where there are several diamond mines. Namibia, which is the major diamond producing country in the world, also has the largest uranium mine in the world.

Namib-Naukluft National Park covers an area of 19,135 square miles (49,574 square kilometers). In this territory of savannas, prairies, plains of quartz and gypsum, mountains of granite, canyons and immense dunes live herds of zebras, South African great antelopes, gazelles, and ostriches. There are five regions in the park: Namib (the oldest desert in the world), Sandvis, Naukluft, Sesriem Canyon, and Sossus Vlei. The next day we went to the sandy zone, where the reddish dunes contrasted with the blue sky. We were in Sossus Vlei, the highest sand dunes in the world, some of them surpassing heights of 950 feet (300 meters). Our Nissan could only climb to a certain point, beyond which only four-wheel drive vehicles are allowed. From there we began an arduous walk under the burning desert sun. The climb up the dunes was oppressive, but the view from Sossus Vlei was worth the pain and effort. Exposure to the burning rays of the sun made it practically impossible to stay there for very long, and, as it was nearing midday, the temperature was rising. After descending and then crossing a dry lake on foot, we took refuge in the shade under one of the few trees in the area in order to gather our strength for the return trip. The walk in the desert under the scorching sun with the temperature reaching more than 108°F (42°C) was exhausting. We had parked the car under one of the few acacia trees to avoid the direct light of the sun. However, it was so hot at midday that the windshield developed a crack more than 4 inches long. On the return drive, we observed from close range a group of passing oryx, their long horns circling backwards. That night we rested and appeased our appetite with a substantial dinner, the principal dish, coincidentally being oryx steak, controlled hunting of this animal being permitted in certain sectors of the park.

We left Namibia with the tranquillity of having made an excellent choice. The modicum of tourists and the surprise and majesty of the many and varied landscapes all contributed to giving us the sensation of having visited a unique place on the earth that for good or for ill was suffering a series of drastic transformations. If I ever return, I wonder whether I will find this desert country as uninhabited and free of contamination as when I visited it in 1994, where there are more stars and constellations visible than from any other latitude, where the streets are safe for walking, and where the people are still friendly and hospitable.

19

THE LAST STOP IN AFRICA

Our radio operator in the Médecins Sans Frontières office in Milanje-Mozambique received an urgent message. The top political official in the district for the RENAMO guerrillas asked for a meeting with MSF at their base in Belúa in order to take care of some "urgent matters." The message dictated the place, date, and time for the meeting. It was only one month ago that I took the post as health coordinator for MSF in the district, and during this time I have done little more than resolve problems and correct some of the earlier administrations mistakes.

Once in Belúa I was surprised by the absence of Mr. Majojo, the guerrilla health director. The only persons present at the meeting were representatives of the political and military arm of RENAMO. Tension was growing by the minute as I reproached myself for not having changed the meeting place to a more neutral site. The political chief of the area took the floor and followed with a long exposition during which he mentioned MSF's unfulfilled offers in the past, ending with communicating RENAMO's decision to cancel authorization of our organization to work in the guerrilla area. That decision took us by surprise and I needed some minutes to get over my astonishment. The gravity of the situation was such that it practically meant the termination of the mission in Milanje. Once over the initial shock, I proceeded to explain the process of change and restructurization that MSF-Milanje was trying to bring about, and that included my presence in the district. Luckily, I had a preliminary plan for activities to be carried out in the RENAMO area, a copy of which I left in the hands of the guerrilla representative, who said they were dealing with nothing but "more promises that would never be carried out." I had to give my word in order that they agree to reconsider the decision and to hold another meeting in a week. Meanwhile, we were prohibited from entering the territory controlled by the guerrillas.

The following week was one of feverish activity in order to present a health proposal that would be attractive to the guerrilla representatives. The proposal included the immediate construction of a traditional health post, a distribution system for the medication, the implementation of a training program for local nurses, and the extension of our support to the Carico zone in the north of the district. All the activities had initiation and culmination dates. For the second meeting, we were joined by Dr. Elizabeth Pierre—the MSF provincial health director—who came from Quelimane, the capital of the Zambezia province and the provincial seat of the MSF mission. This second meeting was to have been held in Sabelúa, the seat of one of the assembly posts for guerrilla demobilization, administered by the United Nations' Peace Operation Force. However, the meeting was not held there but closer to the interior zone that was under RENAMO's complete control. After hours of negotiations we finally came to an agreement, but not until MSF promised to carry out the activities listed in the proposal as the stipulated timeframe. The new accord was sealed with a traditional dinner shared *by all the attendees, a dinner that did not lack the gourd leaves or the corn dough known as n'zima, so fancied in these latitudes.*

Within the two-week timeframe, to the satisfaction of the contingency, we built the first traditional health post in Mongue, which immediately went into operation. In the following weeks, other points of the agreement were carried out based on the established terms, although with another type of setback.

MOZAMBIQUE

Mozambique is a country previously known to me only from school geography classes and from a song that the Andean group Inti Illimani sang that ends with the words "from Brazil to Mozambique we all share the same history." I never imagined in those youthful days that I would get to know such a distant place, abused for too long by nations and people in search of power. Mozambique is a country located in the southeastern part of the African continent, bordered to the north by Tanzania, to the south by the Republic of South Africa and Swaziland, to the east by the Indian Ocean, and to the west by Zambia, Malawi, and Zimbabwe. It has an area of 309,415 square miles (801,590 square kilometers), a population of approximately 15.1 million, and the population density of seven persons per square mile. The capital and most important city in the country is Maputo. The most important ethnic groups include the Makua (47 percent), the Tsonga (23 percent), and the Maravi (12 percent). The official language is Portuguese, but the most common dialects are Makua (38 percent), Tsonga (24 percent), and Sena (10 percent). Chewa and Yao, which are also spoken in Malawi, are the languages of the northeastern region of the country, near the border with that nation.

A part of the history of this convulsed country began in the fifteenth century when Vasco da Gama arrived at the estuary in Quelimane. Later, the Portuguese began the colonization of this African enclave. From the seventeenth to the middle of the nineteenth centuries, the

Portuguese merchants carried on a slave trade directed toward Brazil. In 1951, Mozambique became a province on the high seas for Portugal. In 1962, the Liberation Front of Mozambique (FRELIMO) came into being, and two years later the war began against the colonial Portuguese forces, a fight that continued until 1975, when Mozambique finally obtained independence from Portugal. In 1977, the RENAMO guerrillas began their war against the Marxist FRELIMO government, generalizing the conflict until, as I have described earlier, after fifteen bloody years of civil war, in October of 1992, the two groups signed a cease-fire treaty in Rome.

THE BEGINNING OF THE END IN AFRICA

April 27, 1994

After having an air plane reservation for some time for April 21 to return to Quito,[1] it is strange to find myself writing from Milanje-Mozambique and working for an organization that was always a part of my work and social activity: Médecins Sans Frontières of France.

A few days after having returned from my last trip to the south and southwest of Africa, I had a formal proposal to join the team of MSF-Mozambique in the province of Zambezi as the new health coordinator for the Milanje district. The new challenge consisted of restructuring and practically rescuing the MSF mission in this district, preparing and supervising a health program during the repatriation of thousands returning to Mozambique after the closing of several refugee camps in Malawi, and furthermore giving logistic and technical support to the Milanje District Department of Health in the Zambezi province. While driving to my new assignment, I saw the Mulanje area in Malawi for the first time. The green of the broad tea plantations situated in the foothills of the majestic mountainous mass of the same name gave me a grand welcome to what would be the final lag of my experience in Africa. Muloza is the last town in Malawi territory, the place where one encounters the border and the customs house. Across the bridge over the Muloza River Mozambican territory begins and then, after following an asphalt road for 3 miles (5 kilometers), one comes to the first Mozambican town of importance: Milanje.[2]

The vehicle that transported me brought me directly to the MSF offices, where I was presented to the expatriate personnel with whom I would work in the coming months. Fabrice, a 27-year-old Frenchman, was in charge of the logistic aspects of the mission, while a nurse from the United States was responsible for the health aspects until my arrival. A little later, Fabrice escorted me to a house where I could unpack. The MSF residence made pleasant housing, almost at the bottom of the hill of the town, from where I could see the mountainous mass of Mulanje. The exterior was in good condition, but the interior denoted a lack of care: disorder, dust everywhere, curtainless windows, old papers and magazines dropped haphazardly. What would be my bedroom was of large dimension, equivalent to an efficiency apartment. The full-size bed with its mosquito netting was the single piece of furniture in the interior to which I would add, in the coming hours, a table and chair and a little wardrobe, where again I could organize my clothes and the few belongings that I had brought with me. The rest of my things remained back in Blantyre and Lilongwe.

The MSF office was a clear indication of the state of the mission. The pharmacy was filthy, and medication had fallen into disuse or thrown away without any control. There had been no registration of medication or supplies coming in or going out for six months; the rodents were eating the boxes and even the bags of intravenous solutions; dust was so thick it covered practically all of the furniture; the medication that had recently arrived was still in the boxes without having been duly classified and was therefore more exposed to the will of the dozens of rodents and hundreds of insects that made the place their home. It was depressing to see whole boxes of essential medical supplies being destroyed while the need for them in the field was enormous, sometimes grave. The local personnel lacked motivation and could not foresee a long-term goal for the organization in the district; there was no administrative staff to provide support to the technical personnel; absenteeism was common; and "sick" leaves were frequent. Moreover, there had been poor supervision of the government and the RENAMO health posts; there was no control over the supplies that came into these posts; the guerrilla representatives of health received medication without discretion, and the MSF team visited only two of the ten posts where they were to distribute our medication; the activities of training and supervision of the local personnel were at a minimum or nonexistent; the Intensive Nutrition Center functioned thanks only to the working capacity of the head nurse; the Nutritional Clinic as well as the Oral Rehydration Posts were forgotten in the different neighborhoods; the Door-to-Door Campaign, a program of visiting and following up on the health at the domicile level, lacked the necessary supervision. At this stage, I began to see the magnitude of my mission and the short time I had to put the necessary changes in place.

What followed were days of intense activity, since I wanted to bring myself up to date as soon as possible about the mission. At the same time I wanted to visit all the areas where MSF was initiating health programs. It was not very difficult to arrive at a diagnosis for the mission's situation, for it was evident that MSF was an isolated organization in Milanje, whose expatriate members had little credibility with other nongovernmental organizations and the district department of health. Most of the activities were behind schedule, and there was uncertainty about continuating some of them.

My first preoccupation was to make an inventory and to reorganize the pharmacy—an activity that, for the conditions of the place, took me almost three weeks to complete. Simultaneously, I was holding working meetings with the MSF team, with the district health authorities, and with representatives of other NGOs. It's worthwhile to describe the man who was the district director of health (DDS) at this time, Mr. Boné, a difficult and controversial person like those one finds in countries where development is only a word that conflicts with the hard reality of abandonment and lack of resources with which they live their daily lives, especially in rural areas. Boné gave me a rather cold reception in spite of the fact that he did not hesitate to ask me to join the hospital staff. My answer was very categorical regarding the true nature of my functions and the reason for my presence in Milanje, which was to reorganize the district MSF mission and to continue delivering health care and sanitation in government and in RENAMO guerrilla areas. However, I very diplomatically made it clear that in case of emergency, I would never hesitate to lend my clinical services to the hospital should they be required.

Boné started his career as a nurse for the FRELIMO forces during the colonial period, and he continued in this career later during the civil war. During the long conflict, he rose to the positions of chief nurse for his unit, then for the battalion, and later for the military region. Eventually, he was appointed district health officer for Milanje. It was clear that Boné was struggling for power, and his current position was only another step in this effort. He would spend many days in the provincial capital of Quelimane, increasing the number of his contacts and political connections, without worrying much about the urgent matters left behind in the district. His small eyes avoided direct contact with other people, unless he felt threatened; his ironic smile never disappeared from his face when talking with people who were not under his command. It seemed that Boné was always testing his counterpart, searching for a weak spot or for ways of utilizing that individual for his own purposes. I saw him as the kind of bureaucrat who fits better in a government office at the central or provincial level, where other skills are required—not necessarily technical—to obtain power. One would think that Milanje was not the place for Boné, for it was a border post, distant from the provincial capital. However, Milanje was an important station in the repatriation process of refugees returning from Malawi, so it was receiving a lot of attention—and financial resources—from many international organizations. Boné knew that he would gain visibility by dealing daily with U.N. officials, press agencies, and the many NGOs working in the district. In fact, he was taking credit for achievements in the health field in which he had barely participated. Boné was definitely a difficult but charismatic character.

ASPECTS OF LOGISTICS AND PERSONNEL

Lamentably, the logistical aspect at the mission was hardly a model of virtue. All construction work was much delayed, the organization of the storehouse and office was deplorable, and the control of personnel left much to be desired. As for Fabrice, he was inexperienced and too naive to manage the more than 150 workers, and the job was becoming a nightmare. In spite of overworking himself, there were no results. In reality, MSF was an island from which several attempts were made to carry out planned goals, but they were made without the necessary coordination and interaction with other organizations, including those with the government. Moreover, communication was enormously difficult since Fabrice spoke almost no English and even less Portuguese. He took on menial jobs that were not his duty, and he did not delegate responsibility, assuming the simplistic approach that all Africans were lazy and fond of stealing. This was a common excuse used to blame the Africans for the poor results of a mission.

A few weeks after my arrival, the provincial director of MSF consulted me as to my opinion regarding the termination of the contract with the U.S. nurse, a delicate point because the team in Milanje would be reduced. However, I considered the woman's presence as adding to the dysfunction of the program, and if we wanted better credibility with the government and the guerrillas, it was vital that we have personnel whose labors would enhance the image of MSF in the district and not the contrary. By then, unfortunately, the nurse had lost her initiative and the desire to exert herself, while the controversial relations with other members of the team did not help to improve the situation. Therefore, we made the decision to send the North American home, and her position was not to be filled for several weeks. Then

Emmanuelle, a French nurse, arrived, and within a few days, she demonstrated the capacity and the desire to work in difficult surroundings such as Milanje.

Meanwhile we found ourselves in the middle of a dispute with political overtones between UNHCR-Malawi, UNHCR-Mozambique, and the respective governments of those countries. The principal reason: the process of repatriation of hundreds of thousands of Mozambican refugees who had fled the civil war and had settled themselves in refugee camps and villages within Malawi territory. According to the government in Malawi and the UNHCR representatives in that country, after the signing of the peace agreement, it was imperative that the refugees return to their country as soon as possible. The posture of the Mozambique government, headed by Joaquim Alberto Chissano, and of UNHCR-Mozambique was in opposition to a massive return of refugees, since the health and educational services and the sanitary infrastructure were destroyed, and their reconstruction still had not reached a level that would cover the necessities of even those who had never left the country. Here was another example of international health as a component of international relations and as a foreign policy tool.

MILANJE

At this point it would be efficacious for the reader to describe in greater detail the town that would be converted into the center of health operations for the entire District and my transitory home; Milanje.

For the passing visitor who stopped for no more than some hours or a few days, Milanje would seem like a rural town of little interest and even less attractiveness. Surrounded by green hills and with an impressive view of Mulanje Mountain, the small town was spared from the war's massive destruction, but not from the slower although insidious decadence caused by years of neglect and abandonment. A single-paved avenue traversed practically the entire length of the town, and on either side rose the houses of better condition, being new or renovated. The same avenue continued on to the frontier with

Malawi, a distance of only some 3 miles (5 kilometers) from the town. There were two hotels, each one with its own bar-restaurant. The only other building was the National Bank of Mozambique, five stories high, which was being rehabilitated on one side in order to accommodate the bank offices on the ground floor and the employees and their families on the other four floors. The other half remained unoccupied and in poor condition. One or two blocks beyond the main avenue, one can find the typical houses of reeds and adobe walls, as well as the typical health problems of any small African town: malnutrition, respiratory and diarrheal diseases, and malaria. Everywhere children were running barefoot after their siblings or playing their traditional games, while theirs mothers busied themselves carrying water or preparing the daily meal. In this area, the loud music from the La Esplanada bar was replaced by the women's' melodious singing—their voices divided into contraltos or sopranos—filling the air with legendary melodies from the past. The *barrios* were the true essence of Milanje.

At the bottom of the hill, at the southern end of town and not far from our residence, lay a manorial structure that is the seat of the district administration today. This type of construction evinces an architectural style typical of the Mediterranean, and the influence of the Portuguese is even more evident in the interior. The houses in better repair are occupied by the different international organizations: UNHCR, the Danish Cooperation for Refugees, the Christian Council, and Médecins Sans Frontières. Its representatives conform to the expatriate community of the district who, at that time, included international functionaries from Italy, France, Holland, Great Britain, the United States, Argentina, Belgium, and Ecuador (my homeland). The one other Latin American was an Argentinean doctor of Jewish descent, Luis Sztorch, who had earlier worked with MSF for several years.

On one occasion, I took a little walk through the district administration surroundings, which has an enviable vista. I went into a building which, from its characteristics, indicated that it had enjoyed some earlier importance. Upon entering through what must have been a majestic portico in the Portuguese style, I was confronted by the ruins of a swimming pool whose enormous dimensions contrasted with the size of the town. The remains of fine mosaics and tiles still adorned the walls and the bottom of the pool, and the once-elegant diving board rose up several meters to the sky. Thick weeds covered much of the detail of what had been a fine construction that contrasted notably with the rest of the buildings of the area. After commenting on this discovery to my friend Bashir, he replied that before the war there had been not only this one, but also a few other recreation areas on the frontier with Malawi. For his part, Bashir and his wife, Hilda, had been accustomed to visiting Mozambique during their vacations, as had hundreds of Malawi citizens who had found in the neighboring country a place of rest and relaxation. By the end of the civil war, this blossoming tourist industry was totally destroyed.

NOTES
1. Quito is the author's home city in Ecuador.
2. Milanje, Mozambique, the district seat of Médecins Sans Frontières of France, is a town distinct from Mulanje, Malawi.

20

RETURNING TO THE HOMELAND

REPATRIATION

In the middle of April 1994, the active repatriation to
Mozambique began for thousands of refugees in Mulanje
camps, where the Malawi government had suspended food
distribution and later closed the camps. The move was
called "active repatriation" because several international
organizations participated in it directly, providing transportation, foods, and logistic support. Earlier groups of
refugees on their own initiative had begun to return to
their country, especially after the signing of the cease-
fire. That initiative was called "passive repatriation."
According to UNHCR, by January 1, 1994, there were
still 650,000 Mozambican refugees in Malawi, 250,000 in
South Africa, 100,000 in Zimbabwe, 22,000 in Zambia,
20,000 in Tanzania, and 18,000 refugees in Swaziland.
One can estimate that by the same date more than
650,000 refugees had already returned to Mozambique.
They arrived in Milanje in a caravan of buses, thousands
of them each week, temporarily housed in a sector known
as "Barrio 10," and from there, after a maximum of three
to five days, they were sent to their final destinations
within or around Zambezia province.
    This experience was very enlightening for me, because
I was participating in the second stage of the refugee

drama; the long-awaited but fearful return. In Malawi, I worked with people who had fled their country because of the continuing war and violence. These people who were searching for refuge in a country that for its proximity and its open-door policy, they were received and given the possibility of survival. As I have described in the first part of this narrative, the refugee was then converted into an individual who, directly or indirectly, depended upon external aid. Life developed within the limits of the refugee camps. With the repatriation process, the destiny of thousands of refugees laid once more on the hands of politicians and outsiders who saw it as another arena for their power struggle.

As Barrio 10 was considered a transitory camp, prolonging the stay of the repatriated or the displaced was a pronouncement to be avoided by all means. Therefore, food rations were not delivered, and registration of the arrivals was accelerated in order to speed up their transport to their final destination. Only after arriving at the last stage of their journey did UNHCR begin to deliver seeds and farm and kitchen implements so that the refugees could begin their new life. UNHCR also delivered food rations till the harvest, when the refugees could become self-sufficient. The object of this policy was to keep these people from becoming accustomed to camp life, where they were totally dependent on external aid, resisting the repatriation process even more. Later on we began to receive the so-called "vulnerables," the group of refugees who, because of age, physical infirmity, or family situation, found themselves at a disadvantage compared with their compatriots. This group, which included the blind, the elderly, the war mutilated, orphans, and adolescent mothers began to arrive in our district, and it became necessary to prepare a transitory center away from Barrio 10 for them. Their vulnerability afforded them the right to receive food rations and special attention, and it seemed appropriate to separate them from the other returnees in order to avoid envy. After a meeting with UNHCR, Médecins Sans Frontières agreed to construct the necessary buildings, the health post, and sanitation battery, which included latrines and a portable tank to store water for human consumption. The center was located in Aleixo; a tiny town located some 6 miles (10 kilometers) from the district seat.

MORE WORK

Within a few weeks I found myself completely immersed in my new duties. We began by reorganizing the office—as much in the physical as in the technical and administrative sense. After RENAMO's threat to bar MSF from its territory, activities multiplied and MSF teams, divided into brigades, worked simultaneously on the reconstruction of health posts, latrines, and wells in the government zone as well as in that of the guerrillas. We restructured the medication distribution system with the object of having more control over the medication that left the MSF storeroom and of monitoring their use in the health posts. Working together with the Ministry of Health, we introduced a form to record data on morbidity and mortality. We presented a draft to the guerrilla representative for his feedback, and by the next month the health workers in RENAMO and government-controlled areas were using this new form. The idea was to collect important health information in a standardized way so that government, guerrilla, and MSF officials would be able to use it.

Later, we began a training program for the community nurses and nurse's aides to maximize the potential of these indispensable health care personnel working in the field. We also trained nine health promoters to increase the number of oral rehydration sites in the barrios of Milanje and to improve the follow up surveillance for the discharged patients from the Intensive Nutrition Center. The oral rehydration therapy (ORT) points were the first levels of care for those people suffering from diarrheal diseases, including cholera. The volunteer health promoter trained to prepare and administer oral rehydration solution, to educate the population about its benefits, and to distribute oral salts to community members. By strategically positioning these posts in key locations in each barrio, we tried to provide prompt access to primary health care to residents living in the area. During the cholera season, the ORT points provided critical support to the Cholera Unit by delivering initial—sometimes life saving—early rehydration to patients suffering from this diarrheal disease. The health promoters did not receive a salary; instead they received some incentives such as raincoats, gumboots, and soap bars. Undoubtedly, the ORT points proved to be effective and very efficient.

Encouraging social participation became an important aspect of our program, as the following scenes from my field diary recorded.

UNHCR did not include in its budget the reconstruction of Chitambo Health Post, which is located in a government-controlled area. However, this post attended the highest number of consultations compared with other FRELIMO centers, although its physical conditions were deplorable. The war-torn edifice was falling apart, piece-by-piece, and the nurse was forced to move to what used to be a small storeroom. Sitting on a crate, he continued giving consultations, while the patients could barely stand up without hitting their heads against the low ceiling. Physical examinations were out of the question in such a small place. His request for a new building reached MSF, but UNHCR did not want to assume the total cost and they were our main financial sponsors. I decided to call a meeting whose attendants would include local chiefs, health personnel, and community leaders within the area. Together we examined the various alternatives and took the decision of building a health post using local hands and traditional materials. MSF, through a donation from UNHCR, contributed gum poles to support the structure and plastic sheets to place under the grass roof to make it impermeable. Two weeks later, with music and dancing, we celebrated the opening of the traditional health post. Its adobe and reed walls, grass roof, and gum poles harmonized with the surrounding environment, while it provided good shade and a refreshing escape from the African heat.

A month later, MSF completed construction (or reconstruction) on two health centers. However, during my field visits I saw nurses still working in the old, partly destroyed buildings. They explained that Boné would not let them work in the new centers until they were officially inaugurated, even if that meant waiting for several more weeks. Upon questioning Boné about this decision, he responded that he was expecting the visit from the provincial health director, and that he would open the health centers in Tengua and Mongue. He was playing politics again and preferred to wait whatever time was necessary until he could obtain full credit and visibility in front of the provincial health authority. However, the visit had been postponed over and over again, so that the next time I went to Quelimane I took advantage of the trip to meet with the director and obtained written authorization from him to start using the new facilities. Boné was not happy to comply with the order, but he had no choice. He lost this battle, but soon he was struggling for power on a different front.

The patient referral system was inadequate, so it was necessary to redesign it. Most of the patients who required specialized care were referred to Mulanje Hospital in Malawi, while the local hospital dealt with ambulatory care, keeping only a few in-patients. I was curious to know why the majority of patients came from government-controlled areas. I thought immediately of the longer distance and of their difficulty in finding transport as two major reasons. However, I never imagined that there could be a third major cause: RENAMO did not allow those people living under its jurisdiction to go into FRELIMO areas, even if they needed medical care. When our immunization team visited a RENAMO village, where we had reports of possible chicken pox cases, I was asked to examine a man with severe skin lesions on his body. My presumptive diagnosis was secondary syphilis, and I advised the immediate referral of the man to the Milanje District Hospital for further examination. RENAMO's political attaché, who was supposed to accompany any outside team, refused to grant permission for the patient to leave, but after noticing the severity of the case he changed his mind. The next step was to persuade the patient himself and his family, for they were not totally convinced that RENAMO would not take action against those relatives staying in the village. After long discussions, they finally agreed to go to Milanje, and we took the man and his wife in one of our vehicles. When we arrived at the hospital, I personally prepared the admission report. Two days later, he disappeared from the ward. A nurse recalled hearing the man complaining to his wife about the mistake they both had made by leaving their village and subjecting their relatives to reprisals from the local RENAMO authorities.

I believed that approaching the health representatives from the two factions and bringing them together could minimize these types of situations, particularly regarding health care. After several talks with each party, they finally agreed to attend a joint meeting. This was a major source of satisfaction for me, but at the same time a great responsibility, for the consequences of this encounter would have significant repercussions, and failure could bring down what little cohesiveness we had gradually achieved over several months. The first meeting was held in the Mongue area. Mr. Boné, the district health director, was not very pleased with the idea that he must attend a meeting in RENAMO's territory, but he finally gave in. During this first meeting, and subsequent meetings in Milanje and Carico, we established a timetable of joint activities, reached an accord for the government vaccination teams to receive adequate support in RENAMO areas during the vaccination phases, persuaded the government representative to admit guerrilla health personnel to the training seminars, and received RENAMO's authorization that patients who needed referral to the district hospital could be taken there without fear of reprisals against them or their families.

As described earlier, I see technical cooperation as a series of reactions that occur in a particular setting, its principal actors being local organizations and local individuals, with the "expert" and the consulting agency being merely catalysts to trigger a desired outcome. MSF's role in setting this series of meetings between health representatives from two antagonist parties illustrates the importance of involving local counterparts in the resolution of common problems.

Later on, we extended our health activities to the Carico area, a region where a health brigade was arriving after more than a decade's absence. There was a long line of sick people waiting to receive specialized medical attention for the first time after so many years. The nurses we saw in this rustic health post had done what they could with the little supplies they eventually received. We soon discovered that their training was minimal, and that only the chief nurse had received some formal training in the past. The original purpose of this first trip to Carico was to make an approach in a zone heretofore unknown to MSF and to observe the area's health situation directly. However, faced with the number of townsfolk who were waiting for medical attention, we organized a consultation system in the health post, where Emmanuelle, the new French nurse, and Esteban, a Mozambican nurse MSF had hired in Quelimane, would attend to them. Only those patients with the most difficult illnesses to diagnose or treat came to me, after having passed through the other two filters. We dispensed medical prescriptions on departure, the medication coming from the first shipment of supplies that MSF delivered to the post as part of the accord signed with the guerrilla leaders.

U.N. Operations in Mozambique - ONUMOZ

In October 4, 1992, Joaquim Alberto Chissano, President of the Republic of Mozambique, and Alfonso Dakhalama, President of Resistencia Nacional Mozambicana (RENAMO) signed in Rome the General Peace Agreement which called for United Nations participation in monitoring the implementation of the Agreement, in providing technical assistance for the general elections, and in monitoring those elections. The two leaders acceded to strong international pressure and, perhaps more importantly, to a series of events that ended up in convincing them that a military victory by either of the two sides was a long way from becoming a reality. To the destruction of almost all of the basic infrastructure, the collapse of an economy that never was stable, and the exhaustion of the civilian population tired of so many years of combat were added the grave effects of one of the worst droughts of recent years which affected the central and southern parts of the African continent, producing a hunger that only with external aid could be somewhat mitigated. On December 3, 1992, the U.N. Secretary-General Boutros Boutros-Ghali submitted to the Security Council his report, in which he presented a detailed operational plan for the United Nations Operation in Mozambique (ONUMOZ). In recommending the establishment of ONUMOZ, the Secretary- General stated that "in the light of recent experiences elsewhere, the recommendations in the present report may be thought to invite the international community to take a risk. I believe that the risk is worth taking, but I cannot disguise that it exists." By its Resolution 797, the Security Council approved the establishment of ONUMOZ until October 31, 1993.

The mandate of ONUMOZ included four elements: political, military, electoral, and humanitarian. Without sufficient humanitarian aid, especially food supplies, the security situation in the country might deteriorate and the demobilization process might stall. Without adequate military protection, the humanitarian aid would not reach its destination. Without sufficient progress in the political area, the confidence required for the disarmament and rehabilitation process would not exist. On the other hand, the electoral process required prompt demobilization and formation of the new armed forces.

In terms of military aspects, ONUMOZ was to monitor and verify the cease-fire, the separation and concentration of forces of the two parties, their demobilization and the collection, storage and destruction of weapons, monitor and verify the complete withdrawal of foreign forces, provide security in the four transport corridors, monitor and verify the disbanding of private and irregular armed groups, authorize security arrangements for vital infrastructures, and provide security for United Nations and other international activities in support of the peace process. Verification of the terms of the cease-fire would be carried out mainly by teams of U.N. military observers at forty-nine assembly areas in three military regions and elsewhere in the field. The peace accord set out two objectives for international humanitarian assistance to Mozambique: (1) to serve as an instrument of reconciliation, and (2) to assist the return of people displaced by war and hunger. ONUMOZ and UNHCR were to coordinate the distribution of food and relief supplies donated by the United Nations Office for the Coordination of Humanitarian Assistance (UNOHAC) for the demobilizing soldiers.

By May 1993, ONUMOZ was fully deployed. The Security Council urged the parties to commence troop assembly in November 1993 and to initiate demobilization by January 1994. However, there were alleged cease-fire violations, and a deep mistrust was still evident between the two sides. After a series of lengthy negotiations, troop movement into mobilization camps had formally commenced. On November 30, 1993, the initial twenty of the total forty-nine assembly areas were opened (twelve for the government and eight for RENAMO), and troop assembly began. Fifteen additional assembly areas opened on December 20. In Milanje district, there were two assembly areas: Sabelua for RENAMO fighters and Milanje for the government soldiers. These assemblies had three or four military officers from different countries who were in charge of coordinating soldier demobilization. In fact, the officers had no authority over the concentrated fighters and could only "advise" the local officers in order to ensure order within the camps. As we saw later, this situation did not help to resolve the different problems that arose in almost all the demobilization camps. I got to know the observers working in Milanje well: The Russian colonel in command, as big and hairy as a bear, spoke little English, and, when off-duty, he was happy to share his vodka with his fellow officers and guests. The other two officers came from India and Brazil, and both were quite friendly, especially Mayor Cunha from Rio de Janeiro.

Within a few months, Mozambique had become the biggest and the costliest of U.N. peace mission. According to 1993 calculations, it took an average of one million U.S. dollars a day to cover the costs of this peace force. In 1994, ONUMOZ's rough cost to the United Nations was approximately $294.8 million. To monitor the electoral process, groups of international observers under the auspices of the U.N. began to arrive in the country. Ecuador was represented by a group of observers coming from different cities of the country who had been assigned to various localities such as Maputo, Beira, and Quelimane. In Quelimane, on the shores of the Indian Ocean, I had the opportunity to meet a lawyer from Quito who was participating, along with delegates from other countries, as an observer of the electoral process in Zambezia province. There were representatives from thirty-five countries around the world assigned as police and military personnel as well as observers for the elections.

21

LIFE AT THE BORDER

LUCIANO AND HIS FIRST PAIR OF SHOES

Luciano, the new guard at the offices of Médecins Sans Frontières in Milanje, could not hide his joy for having obtained that position. I always found him, early in the morning, seated in the wicker chair at the MSF district office entrance, with his foolish smile and friendly greeting. From our first encounter I noticed his enormous bare feet that were propped up higher than the height of the chair, which made for a more comfortable position for spending the long hours of the night.

It was not unknown to us that there was no guard alive who did not succumb to the charms of Morpheus during the night, but at times just Luciano's lone presence was a deterrent. Luciano came from a humble rural status, and in spite of his youth he already had a large family of his own. The long civil war in Mozambique affected him as much as others, obliging him to take refuge in neighboring Malawi, from where he had returned only a few months earlier. His rather fluent Portuguese made for good communication, which made it possible to get to know him better during the following weeks.

Luciano had the largest feet that I have ever seen, feet that had never known what it was to wear shoes. In this part of the continent, only a few children have shoes in their early years, but by maturity it is a sign of poverty not to have them. For Luciano, in his state of refuge, it was not possible to get one of the few jobs that were offered in the refugee camps, and upon his return to Mozambique his priority was to find some occupation that would allow him to support his family. In the brief comments that we used to exchange in the morning, he always mentioned his dream of buying his first pair of shoes with his first salary. However, this dream was thwarted each month, for there were the more immediate needs of his wife and children, such as ensuring housing, food, and clothing for them.

During one of our conversations, I deduced from his slurred words that he had been drinking the night before and I made an appointment with him in my office. There, I proceeded to warn him that he must be careful about coming to work in that condition again, for it would mean his immediate dismissal. A little more in confidence, I began to expound on my doubts about the possibility of his being able to collect enough amount to buy his shoes if the money were misspent on alcoholic drinks. It seems the desire to fulfill his dream of having a pair of shoes was stronger than his compulsion to drink, for that same day we came to an agreement by which, on each bi-weekly payday, the secretary would retain the equivalent of ten percent of his salary, money that would accumulate until it reached the necessary amount.

By the first payday of the third month, he had been able to put together a sufficient amount in local currency[1] in order to buy tennis shoes. Luciano, very excited, came to ask permission to go to the market to fulfill his longed-for dream. A short time later he returned, still barefoot, and with an expression that denoted his deep frustration: He could not find any shoes in the market to fit his enormous feet.... Not even the hopeful tone of the salesman, who had promised to get the adequate size within a few weeks, helped to change his state of mind. Before Luciano could opt to drown his sorrows in alcohol, I proceeded to put the money into safekeeping until the day of arrival of his well-known request.

I had almost forgotten about it when, one day upon arriving at the office, I found Luciano radiant with happiness, in brand new tennis shoes, ready to take some message to the farthest corner of the district. Finally, after an exhaustive search in Tete and Quelimane, the salesman had found the right size shoes for our guard. All day long, all of us at MSF rejoiced over such a simple but at the same time significant occurrence. Luciano's contagious joy was a lesson in humanity, for those little experiences let us look at life from another angle, from the perspective of a simple man from whom all of us have much to learn. A pair of shoes, something that most of us take for granted, was for Luciano a reason for exhilaration, because, for the first time in his more than twenty years of life, his great feet were grazing on a soft and delicate surface that, taking on more than the role of protector, fulfilled the role of enhancing the personal dignity of someone who had done it by means of constant and honorable work.

BEGINNING OF "NORMALITY"

With the return of thousands of refugees from Malawi, the country began to live normally, which grew out of the abnormal, given that violence and disorder had been commonplace every day of more than fifteen years. It was evident that an atmosphere of optimism was slowly beginning to spread. Old combatants reunited in civilian life, and those who had families or a piece of land regenerated their farming labors so long abandoned. One Saturday, I heard music coming from the house adjoining the Catholic

199

Church: an enthusiastic choir was boarding together to prepare the religious hymns they were to sing for Sunday mass. Voices of men, women, and children joined in praise of peace. After the religious service, the Milanje people in their Sunday suits strolled once again up and down the asphalt avenue of the town, displaying their best dress and enjoying their Sunday gatherings.

On several occasions I was fortunate enough to be invited to family celebrations, where I never failed to marvel at the cadence of the Africans dancing the Kwasa Kwasa, a rhythm coming from Tanzania that was catching on fast in the central and southern parts of the African continent. It was a dance that somewhat resembled the Dominican merengue. They played other Mozambican rhythms, and, in the case of those people of better economic means, the music of Roberto Carlos and other less well-known Brazilian performers was never missing from their homes. Local businessmen with some vision invested money to rebuild an old Portuguese club that became the first and only discotheque in town. I call them "visionaries," because there was a growing expatriate community from the different international organizations as well as teams of national and foreign newsmen beginning to arrive in the district who, on weekends, had no place to go to for relaxation.

The soccer championship was reinstated with great excitement, and almost every one of the institutions in Milanje supported a team, including MSF. This well-attended championship was held for the second consecutive time after years of falling into oblivion because of civil war. Through a communal project, the members of the various teams improved the conditions of the field, making it ready in time for the first of the hard-fought games.

For me, all these activities were routine for a country that, as in the case of Ecuador, has lived in relative peace. However, in Mozambique, the achievement of these simple successes is the motive for general satisfaction, because there is a whole generation that has grown up in the midst of war and has only lately been learning to live in an era of peace. Even so, it is a fragile peace, as we will see later, for the presence of the demobilization bases with so many government soldiers as well as those of the guerrillas make for a fuse that could ignite at any moment.

AN INCIPIENT PEACE

There are few countries in the world where the population has such a large number of arms, as does Mozambique. In the refugee camps in Malawi, someone offered to sell me an AK47, the Soviet assault rifle also known as *Kalashnikov*, for the ludicrous price of 50 *kwachas*, equivalent at that time to a little more than US$10. Munitions were somewhat more expensive and difficult to obtain. On the other hand, antipersonnel land mines infested the country and, according to U.N. information, could reach the chilling figure of 2 million. Those artifacts have victimized more than 10,000 individuals, the majority civilian, and the number continues to rise. Bazooka rockets, mortars, landmines, explosives, and hand grenades are the sad legacy of the war. Armed banditry became widespread, and the situation was exacerbated by the proliferation of weapons despite the thousands of guns collected from troops of the two parties and from paramilitary forces.

Government troops as well as elements of the guerrillas were concentrated in different assembly areas while they awaited the moment for demobilization. However, in Zambezia, and specifically in the Milanje district, paramilitary forces still existed, one of them known as "Los Marias," who opposed the peace process and antagonized the government. This group—its membership being an unknown quantity—did not accept the disarmament process. They were tough and ruthless soldiers who, during the war years, had acquired fame for their ferocity and about whom legends were told, for example, that they performed certain rites before combat to turn themselves into "bullet proof" warriors or into "invisible" soldiers able to infiltrate the enemy zone. According to information coming from Maputo, one of the Marias bases was near Carico, where an MSF health post was located for logistical support. The U.N. went so far as to send in a team to investigate this group, but they came away without obtaining any concrete results.

The democratic process went ahead, and the presidential election loomed nearer, although the ghost of cancellation or postponement was always present. In the midst of the political contest, those in international circles did not fail to hide their fear that the situation might become a repeat of Angola debacle. In that West African country, after years of fighting, the government, and the guerrilla movement UNITA finally consented to hold presidential elections. After losing in the final vote, UNITA reinitiated the war, arguing a non-existent electoral fraud. To the international functionaries who were monitoring the democratic process in Mozambique, this was an episode that made their hair stand on end, and a resumption of the conflict was not completely out of the picture. Peace was balanced in a fragile vessel captained by the leaders of two factions who, shortly before, had been savagely fighting for the control of the country, and the peace process that would be consolidated in the coming months depended upon them.

MALAWI'S FIRST PRESIDENTIAL ELECTIONS

While living in Mozambique, I did not lose contact with Malawi and its political, social, and cultural happenings. In spite of communications difficulties, at least once a week I crossed the frontier toward Muloza, and from the post office there I made one or two telephone calls to Malawi or to Ecuador. Milanje did not have a telephone service, so we were only able to contact our office in Quelimane and Maputo by short-wave radio. Every two or three weeks, I went to Blantyre to attend working meetings or to visit friends there and in Zomba. Because of our geographic location we were partially dependent on MSF-Malawi in Blantyre, a city much closer to Milanje than Quelimane, the provincial capital of Zambezia.

During one visit to Malawi in May to attend a meeting with MSF officials, I witnessed the final days of the electoral debate before the first presidential elections. It was very exciting to be able to observe the people of

Blantyre openly supporting their preferred candidates, and colored flags of the different political parties draped the city. The UDF's yellow flag was present in wide sectors of Blantyre, setting the tone that it was the popular sentiment. On the day of our arrival from Mozambique, traffic was horrible on the Kamuzu highway, where MCP and UDF sympathizers were demonstrating support for their respective parties. It was nice to see that in spite of being practically side by side, there were no violent episodes between the factions, and what's more, the single interchange that I saw were jokes charged with irony, which someone originating from Quito would classify as *sal quiteña*.[2]

On Sunday, from the early morning hours on, Malawians formed long lines in order to place their votes. The day came to an end in an atmosphere of peace and tranquillity, in spite of one incident where they found a box stuffed full of ballots previously marked in favor of MCP. The following day, the London's BBC broadcast the nonofficial results of the election, which gave a wide lead to the UDF candidate, Bakili Muluzi. On the next broadcast Muluzi was declared winner. The election results reflected the regional strengths of each of the three major parties: UDF in the south, MCP in the center, and AFORD in the north. The government party, MCP, finally admitted defeat a week later, although celebrations across the country did not wait that long. I was witness to a unique and unprecedented event in the history of Malawi.

NOTES

1. The *meticais* is the official Mozambican currency. At that time, 3,500 meticais was equal to US$1.
2. *Sal quiteña*: are witticisms or "local humor" in Quito, Ecuador.

22

PEACE OR WAR?

FIRST EVACUATION FROM MOZAMBIQUE TO MALAWI

April 1994

The meeting of the Emergency District Committee, postponed once before, was finally held at the seat of the Milanje Administration with the massive assistance of the régulos,[1] representatives of all the international organizations of technical cooperation and the governmental sector. As the coordinator from MSF, it was my duty to attend the meeting. The principal theme was the process of repatriation and the distribution of material and humanitarian aid to the repatriated. The district administrator opened the session with the accustomed formality and introduced the person who would translate from Portuguese to Chichewa, because the majority of the chiefs did not have a command of Portuguese. As the meeting progressed slowly between translations, my attention was fixed on a wide window located to my right, and I exercised my imagination by thinking that it was the single means of escape in case rebellion or some-

thing of that nature broke out. When they were speaking in Portuguese my mind returned to the problems at hand, but during the translation to the local dialect for some reason the image regarding that window returned.

I had almost forgotten those digressions when we became distracted by noise coming from outside that were growing in intensity. In a few minutes the bulk of the soldiers billeted in the demobilization camp at Milanje surrounded the building and were shouting, demanding to see the administrator. When the government representative came forward, the rebel leader outlined a series of demands to be met before they would agree to return to the assembly base. Some of the demands were either impractical or excessive, and the administrator quietly indicated that he did not have the authority to make that kind of decision. To this sincere response, the rebels proceeded to assault him, first verbally and then physically, while the rest of the insurgents—some of who were armed—took up positions around the building. It seems that other attendees at the session had directed their eyes toward the same window as I had, and when the matter took on more violent tones, the education representative waited no longer and jumped through the salvation window, an example followed by a few others, including myself. Once outside we were chased through the settlement, where we hid in the bushes while we decided what to do next. It was clear that the soldiers had been well organized, because the main streets had been closed and the rebels were deployed at the most strategic points of the town.

The ONUMOZ military officers in charge of the camp, in their position as simple observers, had been able to do little or nothing to put down the uprising. As they were entrenched in the assembly base, their actions were limited to communicating the events to headquarters in Maputo and later to transmitting the demands of the soldiers who, after months of concentration, and waiting to be demo-

bilized, were beginning to lose patience. We soon discovered that ONUMOZ, aiming to avoid problems, had made too many concessions in the past, and the soldiers began to deliver lists of petitions that included money, blankets, food, clothing. I remember talking to the Russian commander who, in broken English, explained to me that his predecessor had made too many concessions to the 300 FRELIMO soldiers who were becoming anxious after months of inactivity while they awaited demobilization from the Milanje assembly. All sorts of rumors began to circulate at the base: "If we return our weapons, the bandits [RENAMO] will come to kill us all..." or "...it is not true that they [ONUMOZ] will let us go..." or "...they will keep us in hard labor camps...." Their demands for material goods became more and more frequent, and most of them were met. They even asked for a stereo and speakers for recreation. And they got them too. "Perhaps the music was the only petition that made any sense, because when we perceive uneasiness among the soldiers, we just play some Kwasa-Kwasa music and immediately their anger or frustration turns into exhilaration as their feet and bodies begin to follow the contagious rhythm," the Russian said. This time, however, the music therapy did not work.

Eventually, I was able to reach the MSF house, but the rebel militia was all over the place. I felt the urgency to go to the office to evaluate the situation with my co-workers and to communicate that information by radio to MSF in Quelimane and Maputo. I was able to avoid one of the blockades, but I had to cross the second. The only thing I took from the house was my stethoscope, which bolstered me in asking the second patrol to let me pass as I had a patient in grave condition waiting for me in the hospital. Most of the soldiers were opposed to this in the beginning, to which I appealed to their "sense of humanity" and to the "intelligence" of the leader, who, feeling flattered, allowed me to go *through. Before arriving at the office I found out that several of the meeting attendees had been taken to the base as hostages, while other rebels were confiscating all the vehicles in town. Incredibly, at the MSF office, they did not know anything about what was happening. Francis, the chauffeur who had been waiting for me outside the administration building had fled the soldiers, and there was no news of him. We sent local people in several directions, who later confirmed that all accesses into and out of Milanje were closed, including the border with Malawi. Upon communicating the latest events to the MSF provincial office in Quelimane, they ordered our immediate evacuation to Malawi.*

The problem became how to evacuate. A few weeks earlier, we had discussed this possibility, and we had made an evacuation plan, using an alternative dirt road that does not cross the formal frontier between Mozambique and Malawi, but instead takes a long roundabout. The townsfolk had assured us that the area was not mined, although we had not had the opportunity to confirm this earlier, and, so after making sure that the few patients from the Nutrition Center were in stable condition, and carrying only what we had on at that moment, Fabrice, the wives of two UNHCR officials, José (another MSF chauffeur), and I began the evacuation in one of the Toyota Land Cruiser trucks. Fortunately, our expatriate nurse was on vacation in Quelimane, and so she avoided this untimely flight. Later, we discovered that our departure was just minutes before the arrival of the rebel militia, who came to our offices with the purpose of taking more foreign hostages.

For the next two hours we traveled toward the interior of the country by unknown roads in poor condition until we arrived at a crossroads that again put us on the original route toward Malawi. There, the townspeople informed us about the location of a rebel patrol on the frontier bridge. We left the vehicle and the chauffeur with instructions to try to get through a little after nightfall. A local led us along through the thickets to the Muloza River, the natural frontier between the two countries, and when we got there we skirted a big trench, looking for the ideal place to try to cross. When it became possible for us to make out the frontier bridge and the rebels who guarded it, we made the river crossing at only some 1,600 feet (500 meters) from the armed patrol; the river is deep at this spot, so in order to cross we had to swim and hope that we would not be discovered. Once on the other side we felt a great relief when a country peasant greeted us with "Muli bwangi" (How are you?), which confirmed our presence in peaceful Malawi. From there it was not difficult for us to get to the first town, Muloza, from where we caught transportation to Mulanje.

We stayed in Malawi for three days until the U.N. intervention in Maputo put an end to this first revolt. Lamentably, all the rebel petitions were granted, which infused them with a sense of power that would later come to exacerbate the problem.

New Incidents and
World Soccer Championship

A similar situation presented itself a few days later, when the same group of soldiers came to town with another list of petitions for ONUMOZ, including a demand to schedule their departure from the base within the next few weeks. The soldiers had remained in the assembly base for too long, and inactivity increased their anxiety and frustration. Peace was becoming their worst enemy. During the war, they were important to the government in fighting RENAMO; therefore they received food, shelter, and payment. Now, FRELIMO was fighting a different kind of war, one in which the combatants do not seek AK-47s but other type of weapons: politics and negotiation. Many of the soldiers from the two sides who were not selected to become a part of the new Mozambican Armed Forces

(FADM), felt that they were ignored as soon as they turned in their weapons to the U.N. observers. They were supposed to have integrated themselves into a civil society in which they had never lived before.

Their strategy was very similar to the previous one. On that first occasion, they did not harm the expatriates, although they kept them in the base until their demands were met. The question remained as to what they would do if their demands were not met. We did not want to find out and gratefully received the order from MSF to evacuate to Malawi. This time we were better prepared, and our departure was timely; we drove across before they closed the frontier, carrying our passports and a little handcase of indispensable personal articles in case of a longer stay. We stayed in Malawi for three days until the situation in Milanje quieted down. Upon our return, we discovered that ONUMOZ had finally accelerated the demobilization process in the district's two assembly areas. Every week from then on, groups of thirty to fifty soldiers received a set of civilian clothes and left the base in army trucks headed in different directions. At last, the base began to look empty, and we were able to concentrate once more in our work.

This second evacuation coincided with several games of the World Soccer Cup, an event that until then we had almost ignored for the lack of television channels in Milanje. During that weekend in Blantyre, our MSF team watched two soccer matches in the comfort of Mirta's house, the home of an Argentinean friend whose hospitality transcended cultural and language barriers. Later on, Major Cunha, the Brazilian military observer, employed every means possible in order to be able to watch the semifinal game in which Brazil was favored. The game was scheduled for a weekday at 11:30 p.m. local time, and we knew it would be broadcast in the club in Mulanje, a city in Malawi close to the Mozambican frontier. Cunha offered us transportation so that we would come with him to watch the game, and Robert, an Italian officer with UNHCR, the MSF logistician, and I agreed to accompany him. We finished our daily labors and crossed the frontier before its 6 p.m. closing. We waited expectantly for almost five hours for the game to begin. As a good South American my preferences were with Brazil and the match ended with a Brazilian victory. After the game, we spent the night in the house of Luis Sztorch, the UNHCR chief in Milanje, whose residence is in Mulanje, Malawi. Early the next morning we made tracks for Milanje, where we arrived in time to begin our work. Anything for the king of sports!

NOTES

1.   *Régulos* are the ethnic chiefs.

23

Dark Africa

Traditional Medicine

In this description of my African experiences, I cannot fail to include the influence of traditional medicine on the daily life of its inhabitants. Once in Malawi, I could clearly see the importance of the so-called "African doctors," or simply witch doctors. In the refugee camp markets, especially in Kunyinda, there was no lack of "clinics" for African medicine—rustic constructions of straw and mud, where the witch doctor, or sometimes the quacks, besides giving consultations, sold every type of potion and root that abounded locally. It was in Kunyinda that I stopped to converse with one of those "colleagues" and, after identifying myself as a western doctor, I proceeded to inquire about the use of some of the roots and plants that were exhibited on the crude counter. When the witch doctor was certain that my interest was genuine, he made no hesitation in answering almost all my questions; I say almost all because upon asking him about the content of some mysterious containers, he limited his answer, stating that it was "something from the spirits," a secret only he and the affected patient of a certain type of illness could know.

In another sector of the market, another witch doctor was exhibiting his merchandise on a simple grass mat in open air. The famous gourd containers occupied the place of honor, surrounded by every class of root, antelope parts, and talisman. This man agreed to broaden my knowledge somewhat about the gourd containers, indicating that they had the property of "speaking in different local dialects, in the name of the spirits that they possess." In this way they are used to "cure a certain type of affliction by which the individual has been possessed by malignant spirits." Upon soliciting him to make a demonstration at that moment, the witch doctor indicated that he did it when there was a patient who suffered a certain type of illness, and besides I would not understand the message since the spirits "did not speak the white man's language," that is to say English or Portuguese. The curious thing about this is that Alfred Mahoney, a Malawi health professional and a very serious and responsible person who was accompanying me, assured me that he had personally heard these mysterious voices during a curing ceremony. Another day, while passing through the market, I saw the valuable merchandise in its habitual location but without the presence of the proprietor. Upon asking one of my companions about the excessive confidence of the witch doctor in leaving his unattended roots and potions, which might each amount to the equivalent of one or two hens, that is, depending on their curative purposes, he pointed to an animal bone talisman that had not been there before. The function of this amulet was to protect the merchandise, and no one in his right mind would dare steal anything in front of that object, unless he were disposed to suffering the ills that a talisman could bring down upon the thief.

In Malawi, there is a Society of Traditional Herbalists, which is registered and legally recognized. The sing'anga or herbalist can be found in the local markets and outside the hospitals, with their collection of roots, leaves, mixtures, and animal parts (feet, bones, and desiccated internal organs). They are easily accessible, and they say there is one sing'anga for each 300 inhabitants in the area of Domasi, while in the country there is hardly one doctor for every 36,023 inhabitants. On the other hand, the *nchimi* is a fortune teller/witch doctor who specializes in locating or canceling hexes. In order to be a nchimi, the person must be "possessed by spirits." To a certain point, the nchimi have come to replace the so-called trial of the *mwabvi*, a ceremony performed in Malawi and in parts of Mozambique until early this century. Mwabvi is actually a poison from the *Erythrophloem guiniense* tree that one must drink if suspected of having made a series of offenses. The accused is declared innocent if he or she vomits and survives; if to the contrary, he or she dies from the effects of the poison. In spite of having been declared illegal in 1911, this practice has continued many years hence. At the end of the last century, Dr. W. Elmslie was witness to several mwabvi trials, some of which he described in his memoirs: "Three months ago Chief Chikusi sent for his Sing'anga with the purpose of testing the loyalty of the inhabitants in one of his villages. All the men, women and children over ten years of age had to take the mwabvi. Within a few hours, seven of the people had died.... Through the use of emetics such as sulfate of zinc and water, I was able to save from an imminent death a large number of patients who were early on rushed to the dispensary in search of medical attention."

May 1993

Scott L., a British physician, was visiting Chang'ambika camp. The young man, with an excellent command of Chichewa, gave up a lucrative practice back in London and moved to Malawi where he has resided for four years. That afternoon we held a meeting to study the possibility of initiating a joint program for parasite control among school children. The same day, Mabuto Kawire, the famous sing'anga of the region, paid me a visit. I met old Mabuto during the cholera epidemic when he effectively treated some of the patients who did not reach the Cholera Unit. He provided adequate on-site rehydration to patients suffering from mild or moderate diarrhea and referred to our unit only those with severe dehydration. Scott, a strong opponent of African traditional medicine, did not decline the opportunity to express his beliefs to the herbalist, who patiently waited until the end to say simply: "We will continue tomorrow."

The next day, Scott looked tired and irritable. "I wasn't able to sleep during the whole night. The drums were so loud, they sounded so near," he said. I was surprised for I did not notice any sound that night. Later in the day, the sing'anga came to the Nutrition Center and his first words were to my colleague:

"Muli bwangi [good day], Dr. Scott. How did you sleep last night?"

"If you think you can scare me by hiring people to keep me awake, you are wrong," Scott replied.

"We will continue tomorrow," said the herbalist and left.

The next morning, Scott looked terrible; his eyes were congested and his face was pale. "I'm sure you heard them last night. They were so near...."

The sing'anga arrived a while later: "How did you sleep, Dr. Scott?" There was no answer. I inquired among the neighbors, but no one had heard any noise during the night. The following day, an ill-looking Scott could not continue any longer and waited anxiously for the old man's visit. He admitted to the herbalist that there are things that go beyond any rational explanation and expressed his apologies for his harsh words against the old man's practice the day they met. I never again heard him say anything in favor or against African medicine. That night Scott slept like a baby.

In Mozambique, traditional medicine occupies a place of equal importance in the life of the people, as much at the rural level as the urban. Green, in his report on a trip to the area of Chimoio, described the existence of two basic types of medicine men among the Chitewe and the Ndau: the herbalist and the fortune teller or medium. This last also uses herbs, but in addition works intimately with ancestral spirits from the community, who help him in determining, diagnosing, and treating certain illnesses. The herbalists are known as *madoto* or *n'anga,* while the mediums are called *acata, chiremba, nyamsoro* or *chikwambo*. Those curers who enjoy wide experience and reputation receive the name of *Dota,* possibly a derivative from the English pronunciation of doctor.

The list of ills that the witch doctor is prepared to combat is long and includes several types of diarrhea, *manyoka* being the most common, the *nyoka kusorora* (diarrhea caused by the presence of "worms" in the stomach, that is to say parasites of the ascaris type), and the *chikesoro* (bloody diarrhea). Dehydration is known as *chikahara,* and among its treatments is drinking an abundance of liquids. There are other illnesses for which I cannot give an established scientific etiology, this being the case for *chikamba* or *pringanisso,* both childhood diseases. The witch doctor described a series of sexually transmitted illness that include: *chimanga* (ulcerated genitals), which has a cure that takes a week and costs three chickens, *siki* (urethral secretion and painful urination), *chikazamentu* (suppurative inguinal ganglions), and *soyenga* (chancre). The knowledge passes orally from generation to generation within the same family, often from the paternal or maternal grandparent. It is said that it is the spirit of the grandfather who guides the witch doctor. Those in the Chimoio area reflect the feeling of the majority of witch doctors in other parts of Africa in wanting to learn more about modern allopathic medicine. There is also a predisposition to share aspects of their knowledge and practice whenever they receive sufficient respect. Today, national and international organizations are financing several programs to close the gap between the formal health workers and the traditional ones.

217

The recent AIDS epidemic affects the whole continent and has given rise to the use of traditional medicine, this because Western allopathic medicine has been
unable to find an effective cure for this deadly syndrome.
The negative effects of this custom are incalculable,
because the population continues to pursue risky sexual
practices, with the erroneous confidence that the
sing'anga or the nchimi will know how to administer an
adequate cure in case of contagion. There have been
appeals to the Society of Traditional Herbalists that its
members rescind their advice claiming the ability to
cure "Edzi" (AIDS), and several organizations are put-
ting their forces in the right direction, adding those traditional health workers to AIDS prevention and education programs. Traditional healers could certainly
become allies in the struggle against disease; they have
the ancestral knowledge transmitted from generation to
generation; they are members of the community where
they have deep roots; they have the trust and respect—
and sometimes fear—of the people. If we learn to accept
and benefit from those practices considered effective,
and if the traditional healers realize the danger of certain procedures that have proved to be ineffective or
health threatening, their potential as health allies is
enormous.

A New Proposal

When there were still only several weeks before termi-
nating my contract, I received several repeated offers to
extend my engagement with Médecins Sans Frontières
in Mozambique. Sadly, all the options were long term,
and by this time I was ready to leave the rural field in
exchange for some more urban center than Milanje. In a
meeting with MSF in Malawi in the first half of 1994,
during the time when the chilling tribal massacres
between the Hutus and the Tutsis in Rwanda were
occurring, I received a formal proposal to be in charge of
the health activities for a short to medium term in one of
the Rwandan refugee camps in the territory of Zaire:
Goma.

By then I had already experienced two armed uprisings that forced me to make emergency evacuations from Mozambique to Malawi. About that time, two members of the MSF health team in Kigali, the capital of Rwanda, arrived in Blantyre where I was able to talk with them. They had been witness to the Hutus massacres of all the Tutsi health personnel. Besides that, in the Goma camp the deaths were counted by the dozens each day, and the cholera epidemic extended over all the area. I thought that I had seen my quota of death and destruction in the past in almost two years in Africa, and I found myself extremely tired emotionally and unable to begin a new cycle in a country that was suffering from that horrible tribal war. Those factors made me turn down the MSF offer in Rwanda; I felt that I should not tempt destiny any further, especially when I was so close to returning to my own country. However, one more adventure awaited me in Mozambique and was to be one of the most significant.

24

CHILD'S DREAM END

THE CHILDREN OF MONGOLA

June 1994

The blades slowly began to rotate, accompanied by a very unusual noise in these latitudes. In a few minutes the quick ascent would begin. Milanje's principal avenue and the curious townspeople who surrounded the craft made an uncommon picture for the International Red Cross helicopter takeoff. It still amazed me to see the landing and takeoff of this type of aircraft in the middle of a crowd, especially when I was to be one of the crewmembers. The objective of this trip was singular: to make the first medical evaluation of a group of children in the RENAMO territory, the child soldiers.

In the last decade of the conflict, the RENAMO guerrillas initiated a campaign of intimidation against the government and civilian population with the systematic destruction of schools, health centers, hospitals, shops, mills, and whatever other infrastructure serviced the civilian population. Added to these practices was something much more disturbing—the kidnapping of children—for the grave consequences would last for one or more generations.

Mongola is the name of the main guerrilla base in the province of Zambezia, an impregnable place that, for the duration of the conflict, was RENAMO's center of operations as well as the main training camp for the child soldiers. For years their existence was shrouded in the greatest of mystery and only at the end of 1993 did a member of the International Red Cross receive the safe conduct necessary to visit. From then on, there were rare visits to the camp where a Red Cross official tried to obtain information as the true identity of the children in order to connect them later with some family member in another part of the country. Only an organization like the International Red Cross could undertake a job of such magnitude, if one considers the logistical difficulties and other intricacies of the situation.

The little ones, whose ages fluctuated between five and eighteen, were in many cases forced to be present at the extermination of their own families, as an initiation ceremony, and finally they were transported to centers where they trained as combatants. A combat name was assigned to each child, and for the very young it almost became a substitute for his true name, which, with time, would fall into such disuse, often finally falling into oblivion. Many of the children no longer remembered their family names and only knew their combat names, while others evinced the psychological traumas of war, making it difficult to be integrated into a peacetime society. For years these children fought without knowing even the why or wherefore of the conflict. They bloodied their hands, and violence became their daily companion, replacing their children's games with those of death and destruction.

This is how, as a result of those visits and with the authorization of the head of RENAMO, the so-called Orphan Center was created in the same location where the training camp stood before the cease-fire. At the same time, the registration and identification process for the children had begun. Timothy, a Swiss national and International Red Cross representative, despite having neither a medical degree nor great knowledge about health had already detected several problems that affected the children in the Mongola center, and it was then that he decided to solicit MSF-Milanje for a medical evaluation, a responsibility that I assumed. The process began with obtaining the safe conduct for ourselves; it was an advantage that my name was already known among the guerrilla representatives in the district, which facilitated the process enormously and included, in Milanje, an interview with the RENAMO political head for Zambezia province.

June 9, 1994

At 0800 hours we began this new adventure on board the International Red Cross helicopter, and after a 40-minute flight we landed in the only clearing in a woodsy and rural region, an area that lacked roads. Before landing I could already see a group of children following a little path hardly visible through the trees, and they—the child soldiers—were coming closer to the clearing in a wild rush. We began to unload what little equipment the small helicopter allowed us to bring, which the children picked up immediately and began their return trip to the camp. We followed them closely without being able to emulate their grace and agility, which they made a show of despite carrying the baskets of cargo. After a walk of some thirty minutes down a little road strewn with woods and arroyos, we had covered almost 2 miles (3 kilometers) when we arrived at the old training camp for soldier-children in Mongola. The trees, which rose in all directions, gave the camp a well-sheltered appearance, with the sun's rays filtering through the branches and a green that colored the whole area; all that contrasted with the true reason for the camp's existence.

Without great preamble and after a short introduction to the children, who we called together around the only open space, Timothy began the reg-

istration, and his assistant took Polaroid photographs of the children, while I began the medical checkups. In the next few hours I examined fifty-five children, who presented a variety of pathologies, the most prevalent without doubt being schistosomiasis or bilharziasis, an illness caused by a parasite (Schistosoma haematobium) that lives in water and in one variety of snails and enters the human organism through the skin; later it lodges in the bladder and produces urinary symptomatology, manifested through hæmatic urine at times visible to the plain eye (bloody urine). In later stages, the infection can cause complications to the renal system, and in some cases cancer of the bladder. I diagnosed some 35 percent of the children with this illness, and it was possible that a much larger percentage had already the parasite in their bodies. I took the opportunity of making a study in which I tried to compare the presence of bloody urine, confirmed by the use of a reactive strip. Under the microscope, I examined those that showed positive bloody urine and some negative, the eggs of the parasite showing up in 95 percent of the positives and in 18 percent of the negatives (false negatives). The statistical results demonstrated the validity of this simple test, which employs the reactive strip and simple observation of the urine. The reactive strip, Hemastix®, is an excellent diagnostic element of Schistosomiasis hæmatobium in populations at risk who live in endemic areas of the illness. The implications of this and similar studies are important, given that in the rural endemic zones of Africa, where it is difficult to have access to a laboratory or trained personnel to make the microscopic confirmation, it would be possible to diagnose, with an eighty-five percent probability of success (predicted positive value), Schistosomiasis hæmatobium through the verification of blood in the urine, and in this way immediately initiate the respective treatment.

Other high prevalent problems were acute diar-rheal diseases (twenty-two percent) and tungiasis, a pathology known in that part of the world as "matacanha" or "Matakenya" (twenty percent). The cause of this illness is a type of sand flea whose female penetrates an individual's bare foot and begins to grow inside the body until it turns into a sphere the size of a pea (0.2 inches or 5 millime-ters), full of eggs that are intermittently expulsed. As a major complication, this infestation produces secondary infections such as cellulitis and tetanus.

In spite of the fact that my duty was to make a diagnosis of the health status of this microcom-munity, it became impossible not to do something immediate for some of the children, and so, with my limited arsenal of medication, I treated the most severe cases. In spite of the number of patients and the urgency of time (we had barely eight author-ized hours to stay there), I found a way to converse with some of the children who spoke Portuguese, and so, I learned about personal dramas that would break the hardest heart: stories of injustice, violence, and death told in simple and direct words that made one doubt that they came from a child:

"What is your name?"

"Carlos."

"And your last name?"

"Carlos. That's my combat name."

"Well then, what is your real name?"

"I don't know."

"Why?"

"I forgot it. When they pulled me out of my house and took away my parents, I was still very little. They gave me this new name, and I have forgotten the other one."

"Do you know what happened to your parents?"

"No, but the soldiers told me that I would never see them again."

"Do you like it here?"

"I have to eat and have somewhere to sleep."

"Did you participate in combat actions at your young age?"

"Yes, in some."

"Did you know that they already signed the peace?"

"No."

"What do you think you will do when you leave here?"

(Surprise.) "I don't know. Is that maybe going to happen?"

Finishing off the authorized time, which for certain was insufficient, we began returning to the helicopter, leaving behind a group of special human beings in whose smiles one could read the hope that our visit had generated something and the belief in the promise of a quick return with sufficient "mankwala" (medicine) to alleviate some of their ills and longings for well-being. Left behind are the cartridges from the Polaroid that were used to photograph the children, which now would serve to give some musical interludes, for the little batteries would be used to bring back to life—although only for some brief moments—their formerly silent radios. Left behind is a place of apparent peace, and the greenery and colors that enveloped it, but that in truth represents the most abominable instrument of war, where the innocent child is affronted, stripped of his purity, and finally transformed into an artifact of death and destruction. Left behind is a part of my own being, mixed with the tears and laughter that still resist believing that there is such evil.

Back in Milanje, the magnitude of the tragedy that those young people lived overwhelmed me with such intensity that I kept their faces, their suffering in my mind for many days. For eight hours I had been so preoccupied with my work that I did not have time to stop and to think about the tragedy in which the lives of those children had unraveled. That same week I finished the report on that evaluation visit, which included the respective recommendations, and I delivered it to the International Red

Cross, UNHCR, and Médecins Sans Frontières. Within a few days MSF authorized the acquisition of Metrifonate, a medication that treats that type of Schistosomiasis specifically, and that, lamentably, comes at a high cost. While we were waiting for this medication, I initiated the arrangements in Malawi for obtaining donations of new or used shoes for the Mongola children, with the objective of preventing and avoiding the reappearance of tungiasis or "matacanha", an illness that almost exclusively affects the feet of individuals who go barefoot. In the case of Mongola, eighty percent of the children lacked shoes, and they were the ones who were basically suffering from this skin infestation. Twenty pairs of shoes came from the United States Embassy in Lilongwe, thanks to the efforts of Conny Arvis, the Economic Officer; and another forty pairs came from Dr. Mitchel Strumpf, president of the Zomba Music Society.

The International Red Cross took steps to locate the families of these children and simultaneously, together with MSF and UNHCR, RENAMO was pressured into authorizing the removal of the children to Belúa, an area closer to Milanje and, more importantly, an area accessible by a road in fairly good condition. With only a few days left for the culmination of my mission in Mozambique, in Africa as well, we received the first group of six orphans from Mongola whose families had been identified, and we met them in route to Quelimane to transport them to their final destination. After a few days the RENAMO commander informed us that they had agreed to move the children to Belúa, and finally, two days before my departure from Mozambique, the long-awaited Metrifonate arrived that would later treat all the children.

I did not think that these two years in Africa would have such a happy ending. I know very well that true life does not transpire as it does in a Hollywood film. I cannot fail to thank that magical continent, which I grew to love, for having permitted me to taste a farewell so pleasing and so full of satisfaction. I understand that for those children the drama has yet not ended, and that perhaps the hardest part is still to come, when the children have to reintegrate themselves into society. However, if little miracles are granted, it could be that larger ones will take place later on, perhaps in a future not too far away.

Orphan of Mongola, perhaps you will remember
the day the soldier snatched you away from peace.
Tell me if you still remember the features of your mother,
tell me if you still dream of the life in your home.

Child of Mongola, awaken no more
with that sin of war and sorrow.
How to cure your soul from that fatal trauma;
tell me with your smile that you long to fly,
tell me with your gaze that you hope to heal.

EPILOGUE

In the last few months, great political transformations
have changed the face of several countries in central and
southern Africa. Earlier, I mentioned the unprecedented
historical event in South Africa, its first multiracial election that culminated in the triumph of Nelson Mandela.
The echo of such a transcendental occurrence was heard
throughout the entire continent. Later, after last minute
problems threatened democratic reform, the presidential
election in Mozambique took place with the clear triumph
of Joaquím Chissano, the president of the country and
leader of FRELIMO, the governmental party during the
years of civil war. Just days before the election, Alfonso
Dakhalama, the leader of the RENAMO guerrillas,
announced that he as well as his movement would not
participate in the electoral process because of supposed
"irregularities." Only international pressure forced him
to withdraw his accusation just hours before the voting
began.

In 1994, the political party that had governed Malawi
for three decades, the MCP, and President-for-Life
Hastings Kamuzu Banda lost the first presidential election held in that country. The new president, Bakili
Muluzi, immediately created a commission that would be
charged with studying cases of human rights violations
and abuses of power. In the first months of 1995, Malawi
witnessed to something that only a short time before
would have been impossible: the trial of Dr. Banda and his
old prime minister, John Tembo, for their participation in

the assassination of four high government officials who had committed the "error" of publicizing their opposition to the regime.

Upon reading that unusual bit of news in the January 26, 1995 issue of *The New York Times,* I could not help but be surprised at the rapidity with which things were changing. It is necessary to have lived in Malawi in order to understand the scope of this unprecedented trial. Without considering the results of the trial, the fact that these two people were brought before the bench to face their accusers implies a warning to Malawi's future leaders: There are those who will always remember the abuses and the violence, and the guilty will not necessarily remain unpunished or unforgotten. Malawi has just given a valuable lesson to those nations where power and authority are still synonymous with impunity. Perhaps this reminds us of one country in particular.

A NEW MAN?

An Ecuadorian friend recently told me that part of that person she had known never returned from Africa. Yes, it would be extremely difficult, after bearing witness to human suffering in its crudest expressions, to maintain a spiritual and personal detachment that would allow an immediate return to the routine and the familiarity of life in my native country. One of my objectives in writing this book was to try to describe events that would be impossible to tell again and again without omitting something, without becoming involved once more. Perhaps the reader, on finishing this short recount, will be able to understand something of the magnitude of the every day human drama that takes place on that continent and also to understand the transition that took place within me which those events brought about.

I agree with my friend's observation, for a part of me would remain forever on the African savannas. It was in Africa where I had begun to concern myself about what and who I am, about my limitations and defects, but also about the qualities that at one time made me believe in a confused and insecure superiority. Besides strengthening my feelings for my little and beautiful Ecuador, within a region that is projecting itself towards the future, I could for the first time turn my eyes to remote origins in the European continent and accept them as a part of my cultural identity, for I am of a mixed blood: Spanish and native American.

Never before had I lived with racism as I did during those two years in Africa. The color of my skin was reason for confusion since in spite of being considered a Mediterranean-type white; I never would have passed for an Anglo-Saxon. In this way, I was designated to a variety of nationalities and distinct races: Portuguese, Hindu, Spanish, French, and Brazilian. My place of relative neutrality allowed me to perceive with greater clarity the drama of the individual of the black race who is born and learns to live in a society that from the beginning adheres to the apparent "superiority" of the Anglo-Saxon white. Even within the black race, discrimination emanates from the differences in the tonality of skin color and/or differences in the area of origin. Those who have broader features and a darker complexion are considered "blacks" by individuals of the same race with finer features and a lighter complexion. The attitude of servility towards whites or foreigners in the face of discrimination is an indication of the depth of the principle of inferiority that has established itself within a subjugated population which, in the case of Malawi, only a few months ago began to breathe the fresh air of liberty. How many cases exist of Europeans or North Americans who, after living in Africa for some space of time, often a short time, allow themselves to become intoxicated by the feeling of power and permit the continuation of the vicious circle that will only end when the African population becomes aware of its true potential and breaks the last chains of mental slavery that still binds the deepest beliefs, beliefs that are slow in disappearing?

During a social gathering in Quito, a close friend mentioned that hardly a day passed when I did not refer to the "black continent." Africa will live forever in my heart and, for me, will manifest itself in every activity within or without of my own country. Its hot shadow projects itself clearly and firmly, embracing the most intimate and secret part of my being. I long to return one day....

O doctor, vocé foste amigo de todos. Trabalhou para nos durante muitos meses. ¡Fez bom trabalho!

—Antonio Sozinho
Mozambican refugee

Apelo o senhor doctor Benjamin, porque durante suo servico trabalho muito bem para nossa gente africana. Não obstante que vocé é branco, nos nunca sentimos diferenca de côr. ¡Foi grande amigo!

—Joaquim Vasco
Community health worker

Zikomo Bwana, ine mau ambiri ndiribe, koma ndirpereka mafuno a bwino kwa inukuti: ulendo wanu mupite bwino ndiponso takhala nthawi se tidawone kuyipa kwanu.
Zikomo! ine*

—K. Bakare
Mozambican refugee

Doctor Benjamin, your skin is white, but your heart is now black, and Africa will live within you forever....

M. Chipembere

* Thank you note in the Chichewa language.

BIBLIOGRAPHY

Basch, Paul. *International Health*. Oxford: Oxford University Press, 1990.

Benenson Abram, Editor. *Control of Communicable Diseases in Man*, 15th Edition. Washington DC: American Public Health Association, 1990.

Breckon, DJ. *Community Health Education: Settings, Roles, and Skills for the 21st Century*, 3rd Edition. Gaithersburg: Aspen Publishers, Inc.,1994.

Bristow, David. *Namibia*, 2nd Edition. Ciudad del Cabo: Struik Publishers, 1993.

Burton, M. and B. Burton, eds. *Enciclopedia de la Vida Animal*, Tomos 3,9,12. Barcelona: Editorial Bruguera S.A., 1979.

Centers for Disease Control. "Famine-Affected, Refugee and Displaced Populations: Recommendations for Public Health Issues. *MMWR* 41:13 (July 24, 1992).

Clough, Michael. *Free at Last? U.S. Policy Toward Africa and the End of the Cold War*. New York: Council on Foreign Relations Press, 1992.

Cranna Michael, Editor. *The True Cost of Conflict*. London: Earthscan, 1994.

Gómez-Dantés, O. "La Evolución de la Salud Internacional en el Siglo XX." *Salud Pública de México* 33 (1991): 314-329.

Green, Edward Ph.D. *Reporte del Viaje al Area de Chimoio*. de Estudios de Medicina Tradicional, Febrero de 1991.

Human Rights Watch Arms Project. *Landmines in Mozambique*. Human Rights Watch, 1994.

King, Michael. *The Story of Medicine and Disease in Malawi*, 2nd Edition. Blantyre: Montford Press, 1992.

King, Michael. *The Story of Medicine and Disease in Malawi,* 2nd Edition. Blantyre: Montford Press, 1992.

Kubik, Gerhard. *Malawian Music: A Framework for Analysis.* Zomba, University of Malawi, 1987.

McKillip, J. *Need Analysis: Tools for the Human Services and Education,* Volume 10. London: Sage Publications Ltd, 1987.

Moorehead, Alan. *The White Nile.* New York: Harper & Brothers, 1960.

Morris, B. "Medicines and Herbalism in Malawi." *Society of Malawi Journal,* Vol. 42, No. 2.

Nilwik, W. & H. Sacranie. *Malawi.* Amsterdam: Rosbeek BV, 1992.

Nolting, W. Mark. *Africa's Top Wildlife Countries,* 3rd Edition. Pompano Beach: Global Travel Publisher, 1992.

Organización Panamericana de la Salud. *Salud Internacional: Un Debate Norte-Sur.* Washington DC: OPS/OMS, 1992.

Phillips, P.A. et al. *A Paediatric Handbook for Malawi.* Blantyre: Montford Press, 1991.

Physician's Desk Reference, 46th Edition. Brooklyn: Medical Economics Company, 1992.

Piedrola, G. et al. *Medicina Preventiva y Salud Pública,* 8a. Edición. Parte VIII. Barcelona: Salvat Editores S.A.,1988.

Ratcliffe, John. "The Influence of Funding Agencies on International Health Policy, Research and Programs." *Mobius.* Vol. 5, No. 3. July 1985.

Reeve, P. A. *Common Medical Problems in Malawi.* Blantyre: Montford Press, 1990.

Rodríguez-García, R. and A. Goldman. *La Conexión Salud-Desarrollo.* Washington, D.C.: Organización Panamericana de la Salud OPS/OMS, 1996.

Strump, M. & K. Phwandaphwanda K., Editors. *Readings in Malawian Music,* Zomba: Zomba Music Society, 1993.

UNICEF. *The Situation of Children and Women in Malawi.* Lilongwe, 1987.

World Bank. *Action for Better Health in Africa.* Washington: The World Bank, Africa Technical Department, 1994.

World Bank, *Adjustment in Africa: Reforms, Results and the Road Ahead,* Oxford University Press, New York, 1994.

Index